Buckle Down™

Ohio Reading

Level 2

4th Edition

This book belongs to: ______________________________

Buckle Down
Publishing

Helping your schoolhouse meet the standards of the statehouse™

Acknowledgments

"The Unhappy Donkey," a fable by Aesop, adapted by Alan Noble.

Peanuts reprinted by permission of United Feature Syndicate, Inc.

Charles Schulz photo reprinted courtesy of United Feature Syndicate, Inc.

"Choosing Shoes" from *The Very Thing* by Ffrida Wolfe, copyright © 1928 by Sidgwick & Jackson, Ltd. Reprinted by permission of Macmillan Publishers, Ltd.

"Sam Saves the Day" from *Sky Ride and Other Exciting Stories* by Steven Otfinoski. Copyright © 1977 by Steven Otfinoski, reprinted by permission of the author.

Every effort has been made by the publisher to locate each owner of the copyrighted material reprinted in this publication and to secure the necessary permissions. If there are any questions regarding the use of these materials, the publisher will take appropriate corrective measures to acknowledge ownership in future publications.

ISBN-13: 978-0-7836-6420-0
ISBN-10: 0-7836-6420-6

4BDOH02RD01 4 5 6 7 8 9 10

Managing Editor: Daniel Smith; Senior Editor: John Ham; Project Editor: Shanti Roundtree; Editor: Stacy Dreyer; Production Editor: Jennifer Rapp; Cover Design: Christina Nantz; Cover Graphic Designers: Kasey Befeler, Staci Van Duyn; Production Director: Jennifer Booth; Art Director: Chris Wolf; Production Supervisor: Kelli Rossetti; Senior Graphic Designer: Scott Hoffman; Graphic Designer: Mark Nodland.

TABLE OF CONTENTS

Lesson 14: Tell Me a True Story 144
Achievement Coverage: IT.C.4

Lesson 15: Reading Pictures 156
Achievement Coverage: IT.D.5

Lesson 16: Maps and Directions 170
Achievement Coverage: IT.C.2, IT.D.5, IT.E.6

Unit 5 – Reading for Fun 177

Lesson 17: Tell Me a Made-Up Story 178
Achievement Coverage: LT.A.1, LT.A.3, LT.B.2, LT.C.4

Lesson 18: Words That Sing 191
Achievement Coverage: LT.C.4, LT.D.5

Lesson 19: Writing Your Answers 202
Achievement Coverage: RP.E.6, RP.F.7

Appendix 213

Word Power Log 214

Activity Pages 217

To the Teacher:

Ohio Academic Content Standard codes are listed for each lesson in the table of contents and for each page in the shaded gray bars that run across the tops of the pages in the workbook (see the example at right). These codes identify the content standards covered on a given page.

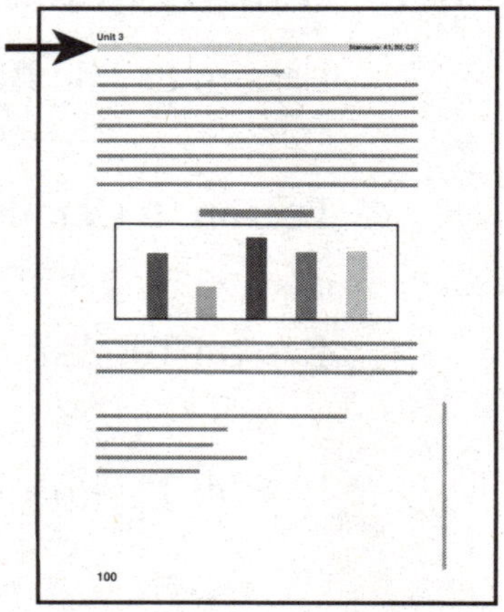

Sample code:

AV.B.2

Standard — Benchmark — Grade-Level indicator

Standards: AV = Acquisition of Vocabulary;
PA = Phonemic Awareness, Word Recognition, and Fluency;
RP = Reading Process: Concepts of Print, Comprehension Strategies, and Self-Monitoring Strategies;
IT = Reading Applications: Informational, Technical, and Persuasive Text;
LT = Reading Applications: Literary Text

Introduction

Buckle Down Ohio Reading, Level 2, was written for kids just like you. It has stories that are true and stories that are made up. You'll read about strange pets, best friends, and what life was like for Abraham Lincoln when he was very young. You'll also learn to read graphs and follow directions.

This book will help you practice spelling, too. There's even a Word Power Log beginning on page 214. Use it to help you learn new words and how to spell them.

Each lesson will ask you questions about what you have read. These questions will ask you to choose the best answer or write an answer of your own. You will also get to do these things to help you learn:

- Draw a picture
- Cut and paste pictures
- Do a dot-to-dot
- Match two sets of things

This workbook will help you understand and remember things you learn about reading in school. It will also give you practice for taking the Ohio reading test.

Test-Taking Tips

TIP 1: Read the directions carefully.

Read all the directions with care. Listen carefully to any directions your teacher reads to you or tells you. If there is anything you do not understand, ask your teacher to explain it.

TIP 2: Read stories carefully.

Read each story all the way through before answering any questions.

TIP 3: Read questions and answer choices carefully.

Make sure you read through all of the answer choices before choosing one. Choice A may look good, but choice C may look better.

TIP 4: Make sure your answer is based on what the story says.

Questions on a reading test are based on things the story tells you. The correct answer will always be based on ideas from the story.

TIP 5: Use key words in the question. They will help you find answers in the story.

Key words are the important words in a question. They often point to where the answer will be found in the story. First, find an important word in the question. Then go back and look for that word in the story. When you find that word, you will probably find the correct answer. You will learn more about using key words in Unit 5 of this book.

TIP 6: Don't let hard questions scare you.

Some questions will be easy to answer. Some questions will be hard to answer. Think about what the question is asking. If the question is too hard, skip it and go on to the next one. Come back to the question later. If you still don't know the answer—take a guess!

TIP 7: Answer every question, even if you have to guess.

If you don't know the answer to a test question, guess. Cross out any answers that you know are wrong, then pick from those that are left. Remember, if you don't answer a question you can't possibly get it right.

TIP 8: When asked to write an answer, write neatly.

Some questions will ask you to write a word, a sentence, or a paragraph. When you are asked to write an answer, think about what you would like to write. Be sure to use your best handwriting and answer the question fully.

TIP 9: On test day, stay cool!

Take it easy on test day. You probably know more than you think you know. If you have studied every lesson in this book, you will have the test-taking tools you need to do your very best.

Unit 1

Letters and Sounds

Can a book talk to you? It can if you know how to read the words. When you read, the words are talking to you as you sound them out.

In this unit, you will learn how to break words into sound parts. This will help you sound out and make new words.

You'll also learn some rules to help you read and say letter and word sounds correctly.

So, listen to this book. It's talking to you!

In This Unit

Word Sounds

Putting Letters Together

Lesson 1: Word Sounds

Did you know there are names for the kinds of letters in the alphabet? The letters in the alphabet are called vowels and consonants. The **vowels** are the letters *a*, *e*, *i*, *o*, and *u*. The **consonants** are all of the other letters in the alphabet.

TIP 1: Syllables are the different sound parts in a word.

Syllables are the different sound parts in a word. Some words have one syllable. Some words have two syllables. Some words have even more syllables than that.

Learn how to count syllables. First, put one of your fingers under your chin. Put it close to your chin but not touching it.

Now say the word *bat*. Count how many times your chin hits your finger. That is how many syllables in a word. Did your chin hit your finger one time? The word *bat* has one syllable.

1. How many syllables does the word *splash* have?

   A. 1
   B. 2
   C. 3

2. How many syllables does the word *grandmother* have?

   A. 1
   B. 2
   C. 3

Achievement Coverage: PA.A.5, PA.B.2, PA.B.9

TIP 2: Words are easier to read and spell when you break them up.

When reading or spelling a hard word, break it up into syllables. Words are easier to say and spell when you break them into smaller parts.

An **open syllable** is a sound part that ends by making a vowel sound.

Here are some words with open syllables:

ma / ma   pa / pa   mo / vie   a / gree

3. Which of these is an open syllable?

   A. er

   B. da

   C. ten

A **closed syllable** is a sound part that ends with a consonant sound.

Look at these words:

al / most   cor / ner   for / ev / er   en / ter

4. Which of these is a closed syllable?

   A. ner

   B. tie

   C. mo

Here are some words with different sound parts. Some syllables end with vowel sounds. Others end with consonant sounds:

ta / ken   a / part / ment   re / mem / ber

un / tie   be / tween   news / pa / per

5. Which of these words has both open and closed syllables?

   A. bet / ter

   B. din / ner

   C. be / gin

TIP 3: Consonants can make hard sounds or soft sounds.

Some consonants can make a hard sound or a soft sound. A **hard sound** is like the *c* in *cup* or the *g* in *green*. A **soft sound** is like the first *c* in *circus* or the *g* in *gentle*.

6. Write the word that fits best below each picture.

   Both of these animal names start with a hard-*c* sound.

__________________ __________________

   Both of these animal names start with a hard-*g* sound.

__________________ __________________

Achievement Coverage: PA.A.5

Both of these words start with a hard-*c* sound.

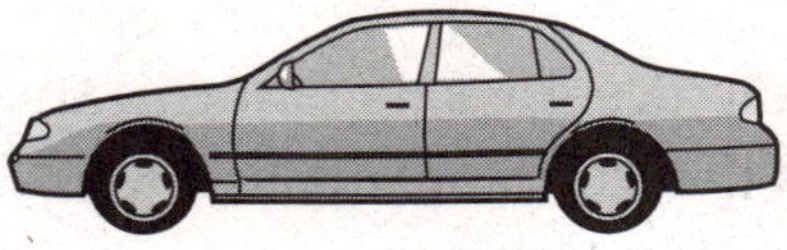

____________________ ____________________

The first word starts with a soft-*c* sound. The second word ends with a soft-*c* sound.

____________________ ____________________

Look at the words in Numbers 7 through 11. One letter is darker than the others. If the dark letter makes a hard sound, circle *Hard*. If the dark letter makes a soft sound, circle *Soft*. We did the first one for you.

7.	cap	(Hard)	Soft
8.	can	Hard	Soft
9.	circle	Hard	Soft
10.	gold	Hard	Soft
11.	giant	Hard	Soft

TIP 4: Vowels can make long sounds or short sounds.

Vowels can make two sounds. A **long vowel sound** is when a vowel says its name.

The vowel says its name in the word *day*. When you say your ABCs, the letter a has the same sound as it does in the word *day*. The letter *a* has a long-vowel sound in the word *day*.

A **short vowel sound** is when a vowel makes a sound that is not like its name. In the word *hat*, the vowel makes a sound that is not like its name. The letter *a* has a short-vowel sound in the word *hat*.

TIP 5: A vowel with one or more consonants after it has a short vowel sound most of the time.

A vowel with one or more consonants after it has a short vowel sound most of the time.

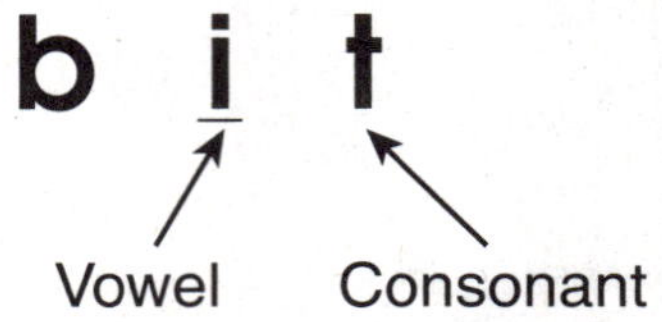

Look at these words:

l**id** **up** **appl**e **hop** **egg**

12. Write another word that has a short vowel sound.

____

13. Does the word *lock* have a long-*o* or a short-*o* sound?

____

Achievement Coverage: PA.A.7

TIP 6: A vowel with a consonant and a final *e* after it makes a long sound.

A vowel with a consonant and a final *e* after it makes a long sound. A **final *e*** is an *e* at the end of the word. The *e* at the end makes no sound.

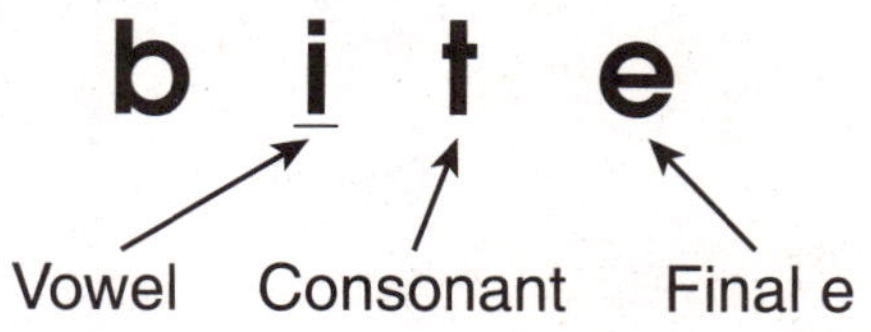

Look at these words:

name ins**ide** **cave** **rule** **face**

14. Write another word that has a long vowel sound.

____

15. Does the word *camp* have a long-*a* or a short-*a* sound?

____

TIP 7: A vowel with the letters *dge* after it makes a short sound.

A vowel with the letters *dge* after it makes a short sound.

TIP 8: A vowel with the letters *ge* after it makes a long sound.

A vowel with the letters *ge* after it makes a long sound.

Long Sound

c a g e

↑

Vowel

Look at these words:

short vowels: badge judge

long vowels: age huge

16. Does the word *page* have a long-*a* or a short-*a* sound?

____

TIP 9: When two vowels are side by side in a word, you hear only the first vowel.

Vowels are next to each other in many words. In the word *beak*, the vowels *e* and *a* are next to each other.

When two vowels are next to each other, the first vowel has a long sound. That's the one you hear. The second vowel is silent.

Just remember:

When two vowels go walking,
The first one does the talking.

Achievement Coverage: PA.A.7

Look at these words:

coat **sea** **leap** **tie** **toast**

17. Think of another word that follows this rule. Write the word on the line.

____

18. Do the letters *ea* in the word *cream* have a long-*a* or a long-*e* sound?

____

TIP 10: When there is one vowel at the end of a word, the vowel has a long sound.

Look at these words:

she no hi be me

19. Write another word that has a vowel with a long sound at the end.

____

20. Does the word *so* have a long-*o* or a short-*o* sound?

____

TIP 11: The letter *r* tells you how some words sound.

When you see a vowel that is followed by the letter *r*, be careful. There are three sounds that can be made when the letter *r* comes after a vowel. These sounds are:

ar	c**ar**, b**ar**k, st**ar**t
or	b**or**n, w**ar**m, f**or**
er	wat**er**, d**ir**t, w**or**m

21. Write another word that ends in a consonant and has the letter *r* after a vowel.

____

Practice Activity

Directions: Listen as your teacher reads a word out loud. Circle the letter that makes the ending or last sound you hear.

1.	c	f	t
2.	l	r	m
3.	z	c	l
4.	a	o	i
5.	d	k	n

Achievement Coverage: PA.A.7

Word Sounds

Lesson 1 Summary

When answering questions about word sounds, remember the following tips:

- Syllables are the different sound parts in a word.
- Words are easier to read and spell when you break them up.
- Consonants can make hard sounds or soft sounds.
- Vowels can make long sounds or short sounds.
- A vowel with one or more consonants after it has a short-vowel sound most of the time.
- A vowel with a consonant and a final *e* after it makes a long sound.
- A vowel with the letters *dge* after it makes a short sound.
- A vowel with the letters *ge* after it makes a long sound.
- When two vowels are side by side in a word, you hear only the first vowel.
- When there is one vowel at the end of a word, the vowel has a long sound.
- The letter *r* tells you how some words sound.

Reading Achievement Practice begins on the following page.

Directions: Carefully read each question. Fill in the circle next to the correct answer.

1. Which word begins with a **soft-c** sound?

   O A. candy

   O B. city

   O C. carrot

2. Which word has a **long-a** vowel sound?

   O A. brave

   O B. across

   O C. heavy

3. Which word has a **long-e** vowel sound?

   O A. bed

   O B. bell

   O C. bean

4. Which word has the same **ie** sound as the the word **pie**?

   O A. friend

   O B. drive

   O C. give

Go to next page

5. How many syllables are there in the word **elephant**?

O A. one

O B. two

O C. three

6. How many syllables are there in the word **chipmunk**?

O A. one

O B. two

O C. three

7. Which word has both open and closed syllables?

O A. bro / ken

O B. ham / mer

O C. rab / bit

STOP

Lesson 2: Putting Letters Together

Groups of letters can make sounds in different ways. This lesson will teach you about the sounds that letters make together.

TIP 1: In some words, each letter says its sound in order.

Sometimes you can hear each letter, one at a time. In these examples, each letter is heard by itself before the next letter is heard.

cot cat pin men mug

In the word *cot*, you can hear the sound of each letter, one after another.

c + o + t

The same is true with the word *cat*.

c + a + t

If we take away the *c* from the word *cat*, the new word becomes *at*. The new word has only two letter sounds.

a + t

And, if we switch the first and last letters in *gum*, we get a new word. That word is *mug*.

g + u + m

becomes

m + u + g

Achievement Coverage: PA.A.3, PA.A.5

TIP 2: Two letters can blend their sounds.

Sometimes two or more letters blend. To **blend** is to mix together. Look at these words:

blue **tr**ee **cr**ash

In the word *blue*, you can hear the sound of the *b* and the sound of the *l*. They mix together to make the sound *bl*.

In the word *tree*, the sound of the *t* mixes with the sound of the *r*. Together, they make the sound *tr*.

In the word *crash*, the hard sound of the *c* mixes with the sound of the *r*. Together, they make the sound *cr*.

Directions: For Numbers 1 through 3, circle the words that blend sounds.

1. bat cry tac

2. frog man hot

3. rat slow sit

TIP 3: Two or more letters can make a new sound.

Sometimes the letters do not put their sounds together. They make a new sound, like the ***ch*** in ***ch**eese*. Here are some other letters that make new sounds when they are put together:

sh as in the word ***sh**oe*

tch as in the word *wa**tch***

th as in the word ***th**row*

gh as in the word *enou**gh***

Directions: Read the following words. If the dark letters put their sounds together, circle *Together*. If the dark letters make a new sound, circle *New Sound*. We did the first one for you.

4. **bl**ack	(Together)	New Sound
5. lau**gh**	Together	New Sound
6. mu**st**	Together	New Sound
7. **th**em	Together	New Sound
8. **gr**ow	Together	New Sound
9. ca**tch**	Together	New Sound

Achievement Coverage: PA.A.3, PA.B.9

TIP 4: Two vowels side by side make one sound.

In Lesson 1, you learned that vowels are the letters *a*, *e*, *i*, *o*, and *u*. Two vowels written together can make one sound.

Look at this list of examples:

ai as in ***tail***

au as in ***caught***

ea as in ***peach***

ee as in ***week***

ei as in ***receive***

ie as in ***tie***

oa as in ***goat***

oo as in ***boot*** or ***oo*** as in ***book***

ui as in ***fruit***

Sometimes, two different sets of vowels can make the same sounds. Look at the words *week* and *peach* above. The letters *ee* and *ea* make the same vowel sound.

10. Which word has the same vowel sound as the word *leaf*?

    A. let
    B. life
    C. meet

11. Which word has the same vowel sound as the word *boat*?

    A. note
    B. poor
    C. boss

TIP 5: Two words can have the same vowels but make different vowel sounds.

Look at the words *boot* and *book*. They use the same vowels but make different sounds. Here are some other words that use the same vowels but make different sounds. Listen to the difference as your teacher reads these words out loud.

most **lost**

low **wow**

The best way to learn how to say and spell these words is to practice. Words are tricky. Sometimes they follow rules. Sometimes they don't. But if you're careful, you'll learn which words follow rules, and which words don't.

TIP 6: Words in a word family have the same kind of spelling.

A **word family** is a group of words that have the same kind of spelling. That means that the beginnings, middles, or ends of the words are spelled the same. For example, the words *bake*, *cake*, *lake*, and *snake* are in the same word family because they all use the letters *ake*.

Achievement Coverage: PA.A.1, PA.A.4

Here are some word families that you should know. Read the first two words in each group. Then fill in the correct letters to make a third word in the same family.

Each box has a picture to help you find out what the word is. The first one has been done for you.

ast

last

fast

c ast

ell

fell

shell

b ______________________

ace

lace

pace

f ______________________

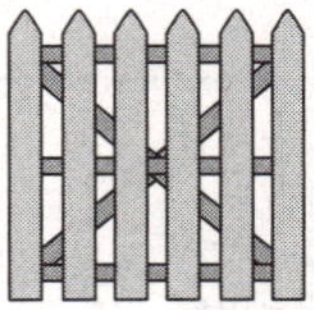

ate

late

date

g ______________________

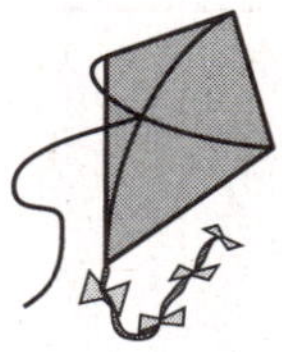

ite

bite

white

k ______________________

ive

five

live

d ______________________

ore

store

more

c ______________________

orn

born

horn

c ______________________

Achievement Coverage: PA.A.1, PA.A.4

TIP 7: Some word families have special pairs of letters.

Here are some more word families that have special pairs of letters. When these pairs of letters are in a word, they make a new sound. Read the first two words in each group. Then fill in the correct letters to make a third word in the same family. Each box has a picture to help you make the new word. We did the first one for you.

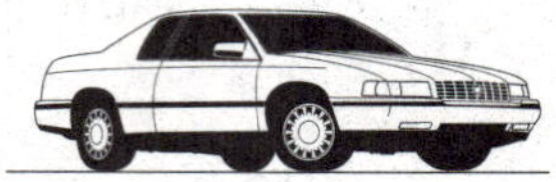

au

h**au**l

bec**au**se

au to

aw

dr**aw**

s**aw**

str ______

ew

n**ew**

st**ew**

fl ______

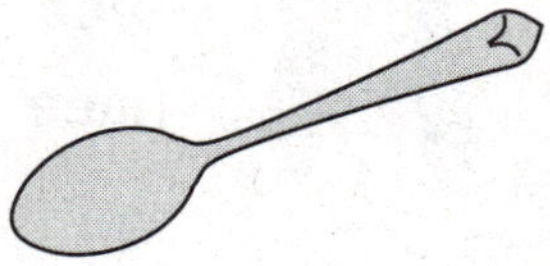

oo

t**oo**

sch**oo**l

sp ______ n

Achievement Coverage: PA.A.1, PA.A.4

ou

cl**ou**d

f**ou**nd

h ______________ se

ow

c**ow**

cl**ow**n

fl ______________ er

oy

b**oy**

enj**oy**

t ______________ s

oi

oil

b**oi**l

c ______________ n

ow

bl**ow**

kn**ow**

sn ______________

ar

d**ar**k

c**ar**d

j ______________

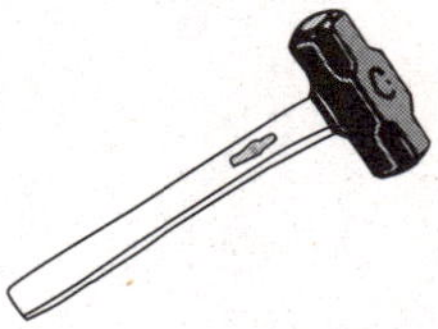

er

flow**er**

sadd**er**

hamm ______________

ir

g**ir**l

d**ir**t

b ______________ d

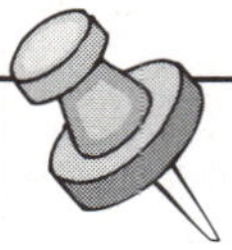

Putting Letters Together

Lesson 2 Summary

When answering questions about word sounds and families, remember the following tips:

- In some words, each letter says its sound in order.
- Two letters can blend their sounds.
- Two or more letters can make a new sound.
- Two vowels side by side make one sound.
- Two words can have the same vowels but make different vowel sounds.
- Words in a word family have the same kind of spelling.
- Some word families have special pairs of letters.

Reading Achievement Practice begins on the following page.

Directions: Carefully read each question. Fill in the circle next to the correct answer.

1. Which word belongs in the **oi** word family?

O A. can

O B. cent

O C. voice

2. How many syllables does the word **magic** have?

O A. one

O B. two

O C. three

3. Which word belongs in the **ou** word family?

O A. sound

O B. slow

O C. swing

Go to next page

4. Which word has the same vowel sound as the word **pail**?

O A. tile

O B. call

O C. whale

5. Which word ends with a **soft-g** sound?

O A. king

O B. change

O C. goose

6. Which set of **bold** letters makes a new sound instead of blending its sounds?

O A. **bl**ock

O B. **ch**ase

O C. **dr**ink

STOP

Unit 2

Reading New Words

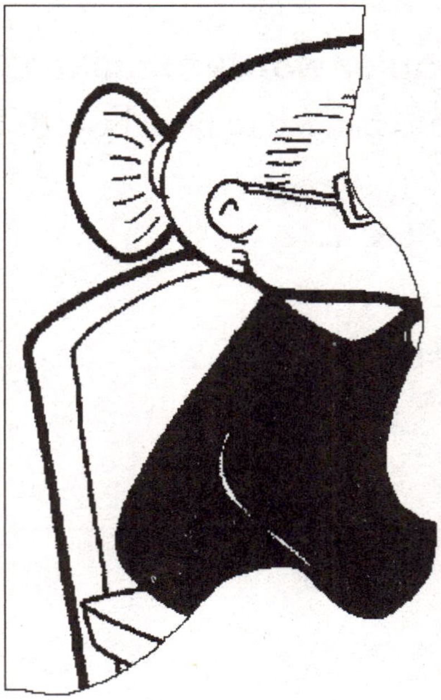

Have you ever put together a puzzle? If you have, then you know that each puzzle piece fits with other pieces to make a picture. Reading can work the same way. Words are like puzzle pieces. When you put them together, you can see a story.

When you read, you might run into words you don't know. Just like a puzzle piece makes sense when it is joined to other pieces, a new word will make sense when you look at the words and sentences around it.

This unit is all about new words. You'll learn some helpful rules for spelling new words, building new words, and finding the meaning of new words.

In This Unit

Achievement Coverage: AV.B.4, AV.C.7

Lesson 3: Spelling New Words

Did you know spelling can be fun? It's kind of like a game. When you play a new game, it can seem hard. But once you know all the rules, it's very fun. Spelling is the same way. This lesson will help you learn the rules.

TIP 1: Words can be singular or plural.

A **singular** word stands for one thing. *Button*, *monkey*, and *child* are singular words.

A **plural** word stands for two or more things. *Buttons*, *monkeys*, and *children* are plural words.

TIP 2: Add an *s* to singular words to make them plural.

Most singular words can be changed to plural words by adding an *s*. Look at this example:

one kite   four kites

Make the following words plural:

1. flag

____

2. tree

____

Achievement Coverage: AV.B.4, AV.C.7

TIP 3: Add an *es* to some words to make them plural.

Some singular words end in the letters *s*, *ss*, *sh*, *ch*, or *x*. These words can be made plural by adding *es*. Look at these examples:

gas	gasses
mess	messes
wish	wishes
branch	branches
box	boxes

Make the following words plural:

3. kiss

____

4. lunch

____

5. dish

____

TIP 4: Change a *y* to *i* and add *es* to make some words plural.

Sometimes a singular word ends with a consonant followed by *y*. To make this kind of word plural, change the *y* to *i*. Then add *es*. Look at this example:

family families

Make the following words plural:

6. fly

____

7. lady

____

8. worry

____

Here are a few more practice words. Write each one as a plural.

9. ranch

____

10. ship

____

11. baby

____

12. beach

____

13. bush

____

Achievement Coverage: AV.B.4, AV.C.7

TIP 5: Some words show belonging.

Sometimes you write to show that something belongs to something or someone else. Most of the time, you add the mark ' and the letter *s* to singular words.

Look at these examples:

Singular

The owl that belongs to Tim is **Tim's owl**.

Add the mark ' to plural words that end in *s*.

Plurals that end in *s*

The school that the boys go to is **the boys' school**.

Rewrite the following words by adding '*s* or '. The first one has been done for you.

14. The balloons that belong to the clowns are the

    clowns' balloons.

15. The bone that belongs to the dog is the

    ____

16. The pennies that belong to the child are the

    ____

Achievement Coverage: AV.B.4, AV.C.7

TIP 6: Some plural words have different endings.

Some words cannot be made plural by adding an *s*, *es*, or *ies* at the end. The best way to find out how to make a word plural is to look in a dictionary. Here are some tricky plurals you should know.

Singular	Plural	Singular	Plural
child 	children 	mouse 	mice 
deer 	deer 	man 	men 
foot 	feet 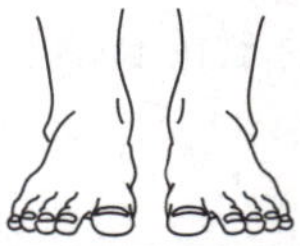	woman 	women 

Make the following words plural. You may use a dictionary to help.

17. goose

____

18. sheep

____

19. tooth

____

Achievement Coverage: AV.C.7

TIP 7: A contraction is a short way to say two words.

A **contraction** is made up of two smaller words. The word *can't* is made up of the words *can* and *not*.

In a contraction, some of the letters are taken out. A mark called an apostrophe (') takes the place of the missing letters. The letters *n* and *o* are taken out of the words *can* and *not* to make *can't*.

Study the following table:

First Word	Second Word	New Word	Missing Letter(s)
are	not	aren't	o
he	would	he'd	woul
she	will	she'll	wi
I	am	I'm	a
we	have	we've	ha
they	are	they're	a
it	is	it's	i

Use the table to help you answer Numbers 20 and 21.

20. **We're** going to Akron.
We're is a contraction for which words?

A. We are

B. We will

C. We have

21. **I'm** bringing my donkey.
I'm is a contraction for which words?

A. It is

B. I am

C. I was

TIP 8: An abbreviation is a short way to say a word.

We can also shorten words by pushing them together. These short spellings are called **abbreviations**.

Here is a list of some long words and their short spellings:

Long Word	Short Spelling
Street	St.
inch	in.
foot (12 inches)	ft.
Monday	Mon.
Tuesday	Tues.
Wednesday	Wed.
Thursday	Thurs.
Friday	Fri.
Saturday	Sat.
Sunday	Sun.
January	Jan.
February	Feb.
March	Mar.
April	Apr.
August	Aug.
September	Sept.
October	Oct.
November	Nov.
December	Dec.

Many words that you know have two spellings. *Road* has a long spelling (*Road*) and a short spelling (*Rd.*).

Achievement Coverage: AV.C.7

Use the table to help you answer the following questions.

22. Write the name of this month using the short spelling.

____

23. Write today's name using the short spelling.

____

24. Write **Oak Street** using the short spelling of **Street**.

____

Spelling New Words

Lesson 3 Summary

When answering questions about spelling words, remember the following tips:

- Words can be singular or plural.
- Add an *s* to singular words to make them plural.
- Add an *es* to some words to make them plural.
- Change a *y* to *i* and add *es* to make some words plural.
- Some words show belonging.
- Some plural words have different endings.
- A contraction is a short way to say two words.
- An abbreviation is a short way to say a word.

Reading Achievement Practice begins on the following page.

R Reading Achievement Practice

Directions: Carefully read each question. Fill in the circle next to the correct answer.

1. Which word is the plural for the word **arm**?

   O A. arm

   O B. arms

   O C. armes

2. Which word is the plural for the word **fox**?

   O A. fox

   O B. foxs

   O C. foxes

3. Which word is an abbreviation of the word **Tuesday**?

   O A. Tuesd.

   O B. Tue.

   O C. Tues.

4. Which word is the plural for the word **cherry**?

   O A. cherrys

   O B. cherryes

   O C. cherries

Go to next page

5. Which words show that the basketball belongs to Joe?

- O A. Joe's basketball
- O B. Joes basketball
- O C. Joes' basketball

6. Which word is the same for the plural and the singular?

- O A. deer
- O B. person
- O C. wolf

7. Which words show that the dolls belong to the girls?

- O A. the girl's dolls
- O B. the girls dolls
- O C. the girls' dolls

8. **They'll** love that painting.

They'll is a contraction for which words?

- O A. They will
- O B. They have
- O C. They are

STOP

Lesson 4: Word Play

You can play with the words you know to make new words. You can put two words together. You can add letters to the beginning or the end of a word. You'll learn about these ways of making new words in this lesson.

TIP 1: You can make new words by putting two words together.

Many new words can be made by putting two shorter words together. For example, the word *goldfish* is made up of the words *gold* and *fish*. Look at these other examples:

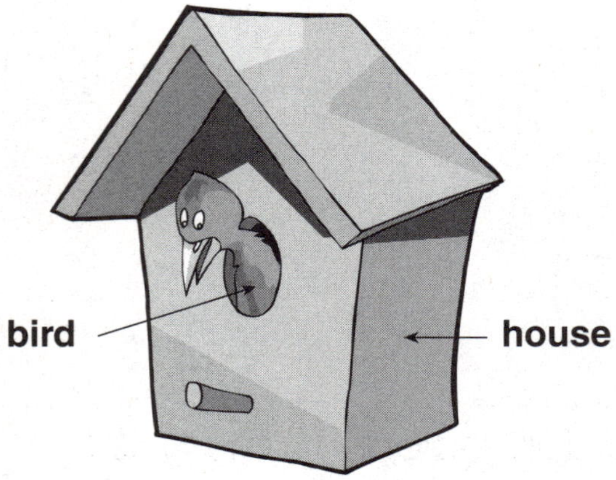

birdhouse

pancake

Put two words together to make new words. The first one has been done for you.

1. can + not

   cannot ______________________

2. down + town

   ____

3. every + thing

   ____

Achievement Coverage: AV.C.6, AV.C.8, AV.C.9

4. Which of these is two words put together?

   A. moonlight
   B. television
   C. remember

5. Which of these is two words put together?

   A. feather
   B. country
   C. bedroom

6. Which of these is two words put together?

   A. library
   B. daylight
   C. message

Look at the pictures. Write what each picture shows. Each picture is something made from two words put together. We did the first one for you.

classroom
____

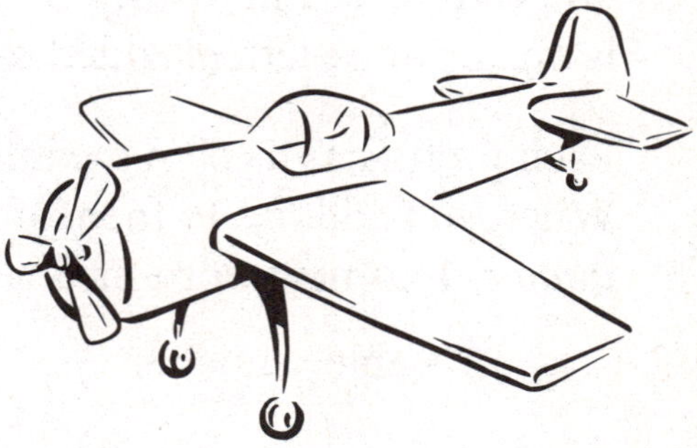

____

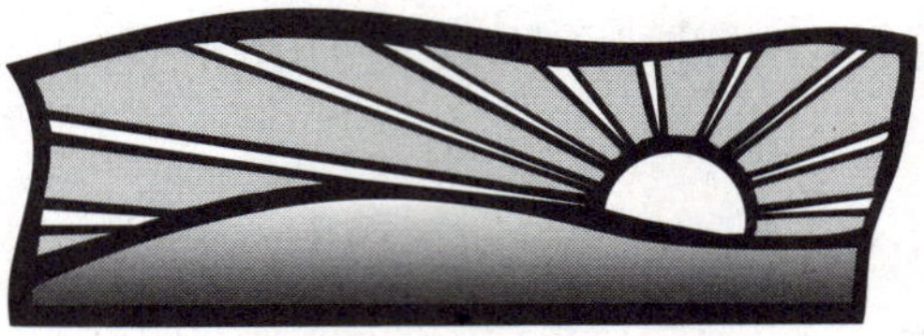

TIP 2: You can make a new word by adding letters to the beginning of a word.

You can make a new word by adding letters to the beginning of a word. A **prefix** is one or more letters added to the beginning of a word.

Each prefix has its own meaning. The letters *un-* make a prefix. *Un-* means not. When you add *un-* to the word *able*, you can make a new word. The new word is *unable*. This new word means "not able."

un + able = unable

Here are some more prefixes and what they mean:

re-	again
pre-	before
mis-	wrong
over-	too much

Achievement Coverage: AV.C.6, AV.C.8, AV.C.9

For Numbers 7 through 10, write the new word. We did the first one for you.

7. re + play = replay

8. pre + cook = ______

9. mis + spell = ______

10. over + tired = ______

TIP 3: A root word is a word you add letters to.

A **root word** is the word you add letters to. Adding a prefix will change the meaning of the root word.

11. What is the root word in the word *rerun*?

______

12. What is the root word in the word *untold*?

______

Try writing new words by putting together prefixes and root words.

13. Write a word that means "paint again."

______

14. Write a word that means "not clean."

______

15. Write a word that means to "fill too much."

______

16. Write a word that means "mix before."

______

TIP 4: You can make a new word by adding letters to the end of a word.

A **suffix** is one or more letters added to the end of a word. Adding a suffix changes the meaning of a root word.

Each suffix has its own meaning. The letters *-est* are a suffix. The suffix *-est* means *most*. When you add *-est* to the word *green*, you can make a new word. The new word is *greenest*. This new word means "the most green."

green + est = greenest

Here are some more suffixes and what they mean:

-er	more
-ful	full of
-ly	in this way
-ing	doing something
-less	not having something

Try writing new words by putting together root words and suffixes. We did the first one for you.

17. Write a word that means "more old."

    older ______________________

18. Write a word that means "most tall."

    ____

19. Write a word that means "full of hope."

    ____

20. Write a word that means "more fast."

    ____

21. Write a word that means "taking a walk."

    ____

Achievement Coverage: AV.C.6, AV.C.8, AV.C.9

TIP 5: Some words have a suffix and a prefix.

Some words have a suffix and a prefix. To find out what these words mean, find the root word first. Then find the prefix and the suffix.

22. Which word has a suffix and a prefix?

    A. rethrow

    B. softly

    C. prewashing

Word Play

Lesson 4 Summary

When answering questions about making new words, remember the following tips:

- You can make new words by putting two words together.
- You can make a new word by adding letters to the beginning of a word.
- A root word is a word you add letters to.
- You can make a new word by adding letters to the end of a word.
- Some words have a suffix and a prefix.

Reading Achievement Practice begins on the following page.

R Reading Achievement Practice

Directions: Carefully read each question. Fill in the circle next to the correct answer.

1. Which word is made from two words put together?

   - O A. mountain
   - O B. weekend
   - O C. teacher

2. Which word means "to try again"?

   - O A. mistry
   - O B. trying
   - O C. retry

3. Which word is the root word in **unsafe**?

   - O A. safe
   - O B. un
   - O C. unsafe

4. Which word means "not having hair"?

   - O A. hairful
   - O B. hairless
   - O C. hairiest

Go to next page

5. Which word is made from two words put together?

- O A. evening
- O B. princess
- O C. something

6. How many syllables does the word **important** have?

- O A. one
- O B. two
- O C. three

7. Which word means "to count wrongly"?

- O A. recount
- O B. miscount
- O C. countless

8. Which set of **bold** letters makes a new sound instead of blending its sounds?

- O A. **sh**ook
- O B. **st**orm
- O C. **fl**ash

STOP

Lesson 5: The Same and Different

Words can be tricky, but they can be fun, too. In this lesson, you'll learn about pairs of words that mean the same thing. You'll also learn about pairs of words that mean different things. Then you'll learn more about the different sounds of words.

TIP 1: Synonyms are words that mean the same thing.

Sometimes you'll find two words that mean the same thing. **Synonyms** are words that mean the same thing. *Happy* and *glad* mean the same thing.

Read each pair of sentences. Draw a circle around the words from both sentences that have the same meaning. We did the first pair for you.

1. Mary is the team's quickest runner.

   She always runs the fastest.

2. When does my favorite show begin?

   It will start at 8 o'clock.

3. Mike has a very small dog.

   Kareem's dog is little, too.

4. Are you able to reach the cookie jar?

   I can run almost as fast as my brother.

TIP 2: Opposites are words that mean very different things.

Most words mean different things. But **opposites** are sets of words that mean very different things. *Clean* and *dirty* are opposites. *Open* and *closed* are also opposites. Opposites can be called **antonyms**.

Read each pair of sentences. Draw a circle around the words from both sentences that have the opposite meanings. We did the first pair for you.

5. The butter was as hard as a rock.

   The ice cream was soft.

6. My father works during the day.

   Tim's father works at night.

7. That store opens at 9 o'clock.

   This store never closes.

8. My glass is empty.

   Your glass is full.

TIP 3: Some words mean more than one thing.

Many words have more than one meaning. A bat is what you use to play baseball. A bat is also a small animal that flies at night.

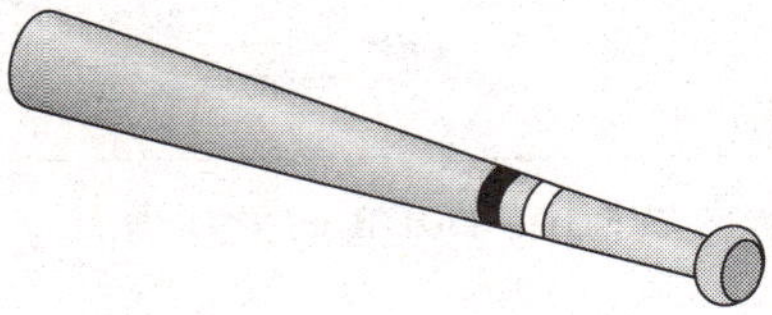

9. Write the word that goes with both pictures on the line.

ABCDE

____

10. Write the word that goes with both pictures on the line.

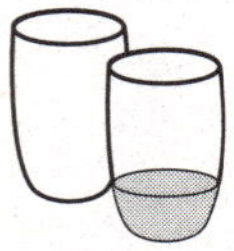

____

TIP 4: Some words sound the same. But they mean different things.

Some words sound the same. But they mean different things. They have different spellings, too. Think about the words *ate* and *eight*. Both words sound the same. The word *ate* means something was eaten. The word *eight* is a number.

The monster was so hungry he ate the number eight!

11. Look at the words on the left. Then, match each word with the word it sounds like on the right. The first one has been done for you.

son	buy
bye	sun
to	sea
dear	blue
blew	deer
see	too

Achievement Coverage: AV.D.2, AV.D.3

TIP 5: Some words look the same. But they have a different sound and meaning.

Some words look the same but sound different. They also mean different things.

Think about the word *live*. You can see a live monkey at the zoo. You can also say you live across the street. The word *live* sounds different in each sentence.

You can say the word *wind* two ways and it means two different things. Look at these two sentences:

> In the winter, the wind is very cold.
>
> To get Joe's toy monkey to talk, you need to wind it.

The Same and Different

Lesson 5 Summary

When answering questions about words with alike and different meanings, remember the following tips:

- Synonyms are words that mean the same thing.
- Opposites are words that mean very different things.
- Some words mean more than one thing.
- Some words sound the same. But they mean different things.
- Some words look the same. But they have a different sound and meaning.

Reading Achievement Practice begins on the following page.

Directions: Carefully read each question. Fill in the circle next to the correct answer.

1. Which word means the opposite of **before**?

O A. after

O B. below

O C. under

2. Which definition of **ring** is used in the sentence below?

ring (ring)	*n.* 1. a band worn around a finger
	n. 2. an outline in the shape of a circle
	v. 3. to make a high-pitched sound

Jennifer woke up when she heard the bell **ring**.

O A. definition 1: a band worn around a finger

O B. definition 2: an outline in the shape of a circle

O C. definition 3: to make a high-pitched sound

3. Which word means "to read again"?

O A. preread

O B. reread

O C. misread

4. Which word means the same as **stairs**?

- O A. floor
- O B. steps
- O C. pairs

5. Which word means "most short"?

- O A. shortest
- O B. shorter
- O C. shortly

6. Which word means to "bake too much"?

- O A. unbake
- O B. prebake
- O C. overbake

7. Which word sounds like **threw**?

- O A. through
- O B. three
- O C. thought

Lesson 6: Learning New Words

Do you ever come across words you don't know? When you run into a new word, you can find out what it means by reading the other words and sentences around it. This lesson will help you do that.

Read this story about a poor donkey who is never happy.

The Unhappy Donkey

a fable by Aesop
retold by Alan Noble

One snowy day, a donkey rested in a warm barn. He had a clean bed of straw and good hay to eat. But he was not happy.

"If only it were spring," he said. "Then I could eat the green grass in the fields."

Before long, spring came. The donkey played in the fields and ate lots of green grass. But sometimes the farmer would ask him to pull a small cart to help with the spring planting.

After a while, the donkey said, "I wish it were summer. Then the spring planting would be done, and I could lie in the sun all day."

Before long, summer came. The donkey lay in the tall grass. But sometimes the farmer would ask him to pull a small cart to carry hay from the grassy meadow to the barn.

"I do not like working in the summer," the donkey cried. "It is too hot. I wish it were fall. Then the air would be cool, and I could play in the leaves."

Before long, fall came. The donkey played in the leaves. But sometimes the farmer would ask him to pull a small cart. The donkey had to help carry turnips and other vegetables from the garden to the farmer's house.

"I do not like working in the fall," the donkey cried. "I wish winter would come. I wish I could rest in my warm barn."

Before long, winter came again. Once again the donkey could rest in his warm barn and eat the hay from the meadow.

Do you think the donkey was happy?

Achievement Coverage: AV.A.1, AV.D.5

TIP 1: The name of a story and the pictures can tell you a lot.

Look at the story's name. It can tell you what the story is about. Also, look at the pictures. They may also help you find out more about the story.

1. What does the name of the story tell you about the donkey?

   ____

2. What does the picture tell you about the donkey?

   ____

TIP 2: When you see a new word, the rest of the sentence can help you.

Sometimes when you read, you see words you don't know. These words may look strange to you. Don't give up! Read the rest of the sentence. You will know some of the other words in that sentence. They may help you find out what the new word means.

Read this sentence:

> The donkey had to help carry <u>turnips</u> and other vegetables from the garden to the farmer's house.

Do you know what turnips are? (If you do, pretend for a minute that you do not.) The other words in the sentence are signs that will help you.

The sentence says "turnips and other vegetables." The words "and other" tell us that turnips are vegetables.

3. Which other words help show that turnips are vegetables?

   A. The donkey had to help carry
   B. from the garden
   C. to the farmer's house

The words "from the garden" are another sign. Vegetables grow in gardens.

4. Read the sentence that follows. Draw a line under each sign that helps tell you the meaning of the word *meadow*.

   But sometimes the farmer would ask him to pull a small cart to carry hay from the grassy meadow to the barn.

5. What does the word *meadow* mean?

   A. river
   B. house
   C. field

6. Read the sentence. Then circle the correct word.

   "Oh, my!" the donkey (would / wood) say.

   Write a sentence using the word you did not circle.

   ____

   ____

   ____

TIP 3: Use word banks.

A **word bank** helps you understand words on the Ohio reading test. As you read, look for story words written in **bold** letters. Then, look for a word bank at the end of the **selection**. This is what a word bank looks like:

Word Bank
bold—dark print
selection—a true or made up story found on the Ohio reading test

Sometimes a word bank will give you the meanings of words you don't know!

Achievement Coverage: AV.A.1, AV.D.5

TIP 4: Write new words in the Word Power Log.

When you find out what a new word means, write it down. Writing down new words can help you remember them. You can write new words in the Word Power Log in this book. The Word Power Log begins on page 214.

What new words did you learn in this lesson?

____

____

____

Learning New Words

Lesson 6 Summary

When answering questions about words you don't know, remember the following tips:

- The name of a story and the pictures can tell you a lot.
- When you see a new word, the rest of the sentence can help you.
- Use word banks.
- Write new words in the Word Power Log.

Reading Achievement Practice begins on the following page.

Directions: Read the selection.

A Day at Wacky World

by Leo Minster

Manny's parents took him to Wacky World for his birthday. Wacky World is a park with rides and games. Manny rode a roller coaster called The Snake. It had **slick** steel tracks. Manny felt as if the ride were so fast it could fly him into the sky. At the top, Manny held out his hand to touch the clouds.

Later, Manny's dad won a purple basketball. They ate jumbo hot dogs. At the end of the day, Manny's eyes were heavy. His dad carried him. Manny fell asleep before they made it to the car.

In his dream, Manny saw a man selling gold balloons.

"Can I have one?" Manny asked. His mom gave him money.

Go to next page

"You can have it for free," the man said when Manny offered him money. He picked a balloon the size of the setting sun. "All you have to do is tell Princess Lim that everyone is in place."

"What?" Manny asked, taking the balloon. The man smiled. His teeth were shiny as steel tracks.

Suddenly, Manny felt his feet leave the ground. The balloon was carrying him to the clouds! The clouds became castles. Their walls were as soft as marshmallows. The balloon carried Manny through a window of one of the castles. Inside was a princess. She was wearing a crown on her head. It was shaped like a hot dog.

"Who are you?" Manny asked.

The woman reached into her pocket. She pulled out a silver snake. The snake smiled at Manny and bit his balloon. POP! Manny fell to the soft floor.

"I'm Princess Lim," she smiled. Her eyes were the color of purple basketballs. "And it looks like you're stuck here for a little while."

Word Bank
slick—shiny

Go to next page

Directions: Use the selection to answer questions 1 – 5.

1. Which word has the same vowel sound as the word **rides**?

   O A. games
   O B. birthday
   O C. hides

2. This sentence is from the story.

   "Manny felt as if the ride were so **fast** it could fly him into the sky."

   Which word means the same as **fast**?

   O A. slow
   O B. quick
   O C. shiny

3. Which word is made from two words put together?

   O A. balloons
   O B. heavy
   O C. basketball

Go to next page

4. This sentence is from the story.

"'You can have it for free,' the man said when Manny **offered** him money."

What does the word **offered** mean?

- O A. tried to give
- O B. took
- O C. talked about

5. Look at the story to fill in the blanks.

Manny dreamed about ___________ made of clouds with walls that were as soft as marshmallows. Inside was a princess who wore a ___________ shaped like a hot dog.

STOP

Lesson 7: Story Signs

When you see a new word, other sentences can help you find out what it means. There are also special books that can tell you what a word means. This lesson will tell you all about these things.

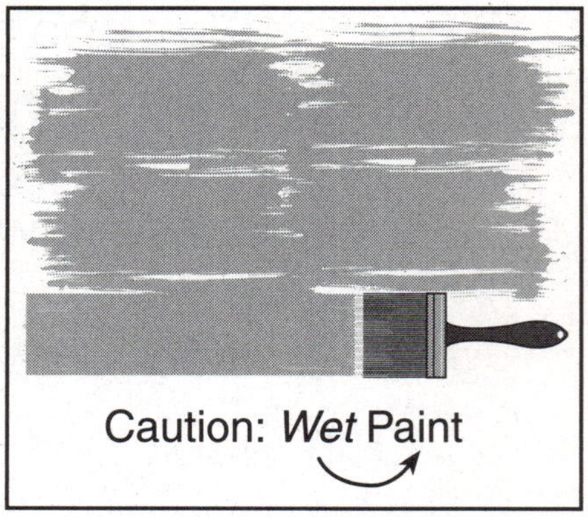

TIP 1: Other sentences can help show you what a word means.

Sometimes, one sentence may not say enough to tell you what a new word means. Other sentences might have signs that tell you what a word means. Look for signs in other sentences in a paragraph.

A **paragraph** is a group of sentences. Writers group sentences into paragraphs. When you see a new word, you might need to look for signs in the whole paragraph.

Look back at "The Unhappy Donkey," on page 54. It has nine paragraphs.

1. What is the first word in the fourth paragraph?

____

The next paragraph tells about a make-believe thing called a "tiffle."

> That was the first time I ever saw a fresh <u>tiffle</u>. It was larger than an apple, round, and the color of a banana. I peeled its skin just as I would peel an orange. And here's the really strange part: It tasted like a grapefruit!

Achievement Coverage: AV.B.4, AV.E.10

2. Read the paragraph again. Draw a line under any signs that help you know what a tiffle is.

3. What is a tiffle?

   A. a kind of fruit
   B. a kind of flower
   C. a kind of candy

Now try doing the same thing with someone in your class. Your teacher will tell you who to work with.

Write a paragraph about a kind of food. Don't say what the food is.

____

____

____

____

____

____

____

Now show your paragraph to the person you are working with. Can that person guess what the food is? Can you guess what food the other person wrote about?

Achievement Coverage: AV.B.4, AV.E.10

TIP 2: Other paragraphs can help show you what a word means.

Sometimes, you must read a few paragraphs to find out what a new word means.

Read the next two paragraphs. Then draw a line under any words that help you know what the word *cancel* means.

It's the first day of vacation, and I have to watch Mrs. Garcia's dog for two weeks! Now I'll have to cancel all the plans I made with Morris for our camping trip.

"Hello, Morris? I can't go camping with you and your father next weekend. I'm taking care of a neighbor's dog."

Think about these things: The boy has to "cancel all the plans" because he has to watch a neighbor's dog. The next thing he does is call Morris. He tells Morris, "I can't go camping with you and your father next weekend."

4. What does the word *cancel* mean?

   A. walk the dog

   B. call off

   C. plan for

Write your answer from Number 4 in this sentence. Does it work?

The boy had to ________________________________ his plan to go camping with a friend.

Achievement Coverage: AV.B.4, AV.E.10

TIP 3: A dictionary can tell you what a word means.

What do you do if you still can't figure out a new word? You open a dictionary. A **dictionary** is a book that tells you what words mean.

A dictionary can give you lots of other information, too. It can show you the syllables in a word. You learned about syllables in Lesson 1. A dictionary uses dots to show you the different syllables.

In a dictionary, words starting with the letter *a* come first. Words starting with the letter *z* come last. Look at this example:

foot – forever 31

foot, *noun* a part of the body used for walking

fore•head, *noun* the part of the face above the eyes

for•est, *noun* a large group of trees

for•ev•er, *adverb* at all times; always

5. How many syllables are there in the word *forever*?

   A. one

   B. two

   C. three

TIP 4: A glossary can tell you what a word means.

Some books have a glossary. A **glossary** is a list of words and what they mean. You can find a glossary at the ends of some books. The glossary is like a dictionary because it tells you what a word means. A dictionary has lots of words. A glossary has words that are in the book you are reading. Look at this example:

Glossary

ice age	a time long ago when much of the earth was covered by ice
insect	a small animal that has six legs and a body made of three parts
larva	the young form of an insect
lava	melted rock that comes up onto the top of the earth

6. What does the word *lava* mean?

   A. melted rock

   B. a small animal

   C. a long period of time

Achievement Coverage: AV.D.2, AV.E.10

TIP 5: A thesaurus can help you find other words that mean the same thing.

In Lesson 5, you learned about words that are the same and different. These words are called synonyms and antonyms. A **thesaurus** is a book that gives you lists of synonyms. It can also give you a list of antonyms for a word. Look at this example:

Page 73

knock	(*verb*) pound, hit, rap, tap
	L
lady	(*noun*) woman
large	(*adj.*) big, huge **antonym:** small
laugh	(*noun* or *verb*) chuckle, giggle
loud	(*adj.*) noisy **antonym:** quiet

TIP 6: Make sure you know your ABCs.

Knowing your ABCs can help you find words in dictionaries and other word lists. Dictionaries and other word lists are in alphabetical order. *Order* means what comes first, second, third, and so on. **Alphabetical order** means words come in the same order as the alphabet.

Write in the missing letters in the alphabet.

A ____ C D ____ ____ ____ H I ____ K L ____

N O P Q ____ ____ ____ U V W X ____ Z

7. Look at the first letter of these words. Write the words in alphabetical order.

   boy fox girl apple zoom

   ____

   ____

   ____

   ____

   ____

The dictionary starts by listing all the words that begin with the letter *a*. Then you need to look at the second letter. The words that start with *ab* come before the words that start with *ac*. Look at this list of words from the beginning pages of a dictionary.

a**b**out

a**c**ross

a**d**d

a**f**raid

The word *about* is listed before the word *across* even though both words begin with an *a*. Why? Because of the second letter in each word. The letter *b* in *a**b**out* comes before the letter *c* in *a**c**ross*.

Achievement Coverage: AV.E.10

8. All of these words begin with the letter *b*. Look at the second letter of each word. Then, list the words in alphabetical order.

   book back bean big bug

   ____

   ____

   ____

   ____

   ____

9. Jason and Melissa have found the names of six kinds of fish in a library book. Help them put the names of those fish in alphabetical order.

   bass goldfish bluefish trout catfish sunfish

   ____

   ____

   ____

   ____

   ____

   ____

Story Signs

Lesson 7 Summary

When answering questions about the meanings of words, remember the following tips:

- Other sentences can help show you what a word means.
- Other paragraphs can help show you what a word means.
- A dictionary can tell you what a word means.
- A glossary can tell you what a word means.
- A thesaurus can help you find other words that mean the same thing.
- Make sure you know your ABCs.

Reading Achievement Practice begins on the following page.

Directions: Read the selection.

Strange Pets

by Julianna Weich

Some boys and girls have dogs or cats for pets. Others have fish or birds. Still others have very different animals for pets.

My friend Bobby has a pet named Lulu. Lulu looks a little like a camel. But she doesn't have a hump on her back like camels do. Bobby rides on Lulu sometimes. Lulu's ancestors came from the Andes Mountains of South America. But Lulu and her parents were born in the United States. Can you guess what kind of pet Lulu is?

People can't believe their eyes when they see Justin walking his pet. Wilbur weighs more than Justin does! Wilbur walks slowly. He uses a snout to smell with. Wilbur has a curly tail. Do you know what kind of animal Wilbur is?

Go to next page

Miss Muffet is hairy and brown. She looks very scary, but Jeremy likes her a lot. Miss Muffet is smaller than Jeremy's hand. She has eight strong legs and can crawl very fast. She sheds her old skin two times a year. She moves out of her old skin and leaves it behind. Then it looks as if there are two Miss Muffets in the cage. Do you know what kind of pet Miss Muffet is?

My pet Speedy looks like a tiny dinosaur. She lives in a glass bowl with sand and stones in it. Sometimes she hides under the rocks. Other times, she lies on top of the rocks to enjoy the sunshine. Speedy eats lots of insects, like flies and crickets. Speedy can move very fast. Can you guess what Speedy is?

Directions: Use the selection to answer questions 1 – 5.

1. These sentences are from the selection.

   "Lulu looks a little like a camel. But she doesn't have a **hump** on her back like camels do."

   What does **hump** mean?

   O A. bump
   O B. bag
   O C. seat

Go to next page

2. These sentences are from the selection.

"Lulu's **ancestors** came from the Andes Mountains of South America. But Lulu and her parents were born in the United States."

What does **ancestors** mean?

- O A. friends
- O B. grandparents
- O C. owners

3. This sentence is from the selection.

"He uses a **snout** to smell with."

What does **snout** mean?

- O A. tail
- O B. foot
- O C. nose

4. These sentences are from the selection.

"She **sheds** her old skin two times a year. She moves out of her old skin and leaves it behind."

What does **sheds** mean?

- O A. wears
- O B. grows
- O C. comes out of

5. Using the reading selection, write four details that tell what Miss Muffet looks like.

a. ______________________________

____

b. ______________________________

____

c. ______________________________

____

d. ______________________________

____

STOP

Unit 3

How We Read

Have you ever missed the first part of a TV show? When you came into the room, what did you ask everyone there? You probably said something like, "What's it about?" Once you know a little more about a show, it is more fun to watch.

Asking questions is important with stories, too. In this unit, you'll learn more about the big idea and details. You'll also learn about asking questions when you read. You'll also practice putting details together to find out more about what you are reading.

In This Unit

The Big Idea

Details

Asking Questions

Putting Details Together

Lesson 8: The Big Idea

Telling someone about the big idea means telling someone what something is about. When you tell someone what something is about, you tell them the big things. Who is in the story? Is it scary? Is it happy? Is it funny? Do the people learn something? All of these things help tell about the big picture.

Before you read this story, look at the picture below. Then read the story name. What do you think this story will be about?

____

____

____

Great Friends

by Linda Austin

Mrs. Corelli lived next door to Emily. She was older than Emily's grandmother. Emily thought her neighbor was very nice.

In the summer, Emily would go outside to play after breakfast. She would pick up Mrs. Corelli's newspaper and take it to the lady's door. Mrs. Corelli thought Emily was the most wonderful little girl.

Mrs. Corelli sometimes baked cookies just for Emily. The cookies were big, round, and filled with chocolate chips. Emily liked to sit on the porch swing with Mrs. Corelli and eat the cookies. They talked about all sorts of things.

Other times, Emily's friend Lisa joined them. Mrs. Corelli taught the girls how to play games she had learned when she was young.

For many years, Emily and Mrs. Corelli were great friends. As Emily grew up, she made many other friends, too. But she never forgot about her neighbor. Emily had learned from Mrs. Corelli that great friends do not have to be the same age.

Did you correctly guess what the story was about?

TIP 1: Find out what the story is about.

Every kind of writing has a main idea. The **main idea** tells what the story is mostly about.

Stories can have many important ideas. But there is only one *most* important idea. That most important idea is the main idea. Your job as a reader is to find out what the main idea is.

Here are some of the important ideas in the story you just read:

- Emily picks up the newspaper for Mrs. Corelli.
- Mrs. Corelli bakes cookies for Emily.

1. What is one more important idea about Emily and Mrs. Corelli?

____

____

____

2. What is the main idea in the story about Emily and Mrs. Corelli?

   A. They sit on the porch.
   B. They are great friends.
   C. They eat cookies.

TIP 2: A paragraph can have a main idea.

Each paragraph in a story has a main idea, too. Think about what each paragraph is about.

Read the second paragraph of "Great Friends" again.

3. What is the main idea in the second paragraph?

   A. Emily goes outside after breakfast in the summer.

   B. Emily picks up Mrs. Corelli's newspaper.

   C. Mrs. Corelli thinks Emily is a wonderful girl.

TIP 3: Look for the main idea sentence.

Sometimes a writer will put the main idea in one sentence. In the next paragraph, one sentence tells the main idea. All the other sentences tell about that main idea.

> Heather ate two eggs. She ate two pieces of toast. She ate a bowl of cereal. She drank a small glass of orange juice. Then she drank a cup of hot chocolate. Heather liked to eat a big breakfast.

4. Which sentence tells the most important idea of the paragraph?

   A. Heather ate two eggs.

   B. She drank a small glass of orange juice.

   C. Heather liked to eat a big breakfast.

Achievement Coverage: RP.E.6

5. In the space below, draw a picture of Heather's breakfast.

TIP 4: Say the main idea in your own words.

Sometimes writers don't tell the main idea in a sentence. They let you find the main idea on your own. Then you need to say the main idea in your own words.

Read the paragraph. It was written by a girl named Jane.

> My mom used to have time to spend with me. Now Mom is too tired to play with me. No one plays with me anymore. They all play with my new brother, Davy. They "ooh" and "aah" at every move he makes. They act like they've never seen a baby before.

The writer does not tell the main idea in the paragraph. Instead, she says a lot of other things that tell you what the main idea is. She wants you to find out the main idea on your own.

6. What do you think this story is mostly about?

____

____

____

____

Think about your answer to Number 6 as you read the next question.

7. What is the main idea of the paragraph?

   A. Jane has a new little brother whose name is Davy.
   B. Jane doesn't like the changes since Davy was born.
   C. Jane's mom seems to be more tired than she used to be.

TIP 5: Details tell about the main idea.

The walls of a house hold up the roof. We say these walls support the roof. To **support** something means to hold it up.

In a story, details support the main idea. A **detail** is part of a story or paragraph that tells what things look like. Details also tell what things sound like, what they taste like, and what they feel like. They can even tell you what things smell like! They tell who the people or animals in the story are. They can also tell what these people or animals are thinking. All stories have details.

Achievement Coverage: RP.A.5

Do you remember the story of Jane? Jane says that her brother's name is Davy. This is not the main idea of the paragraph. But it is a detail.

8. Read Jane's paragraph on page 80 again. Find two details that tell about the main idea. Write them on lines A and B.

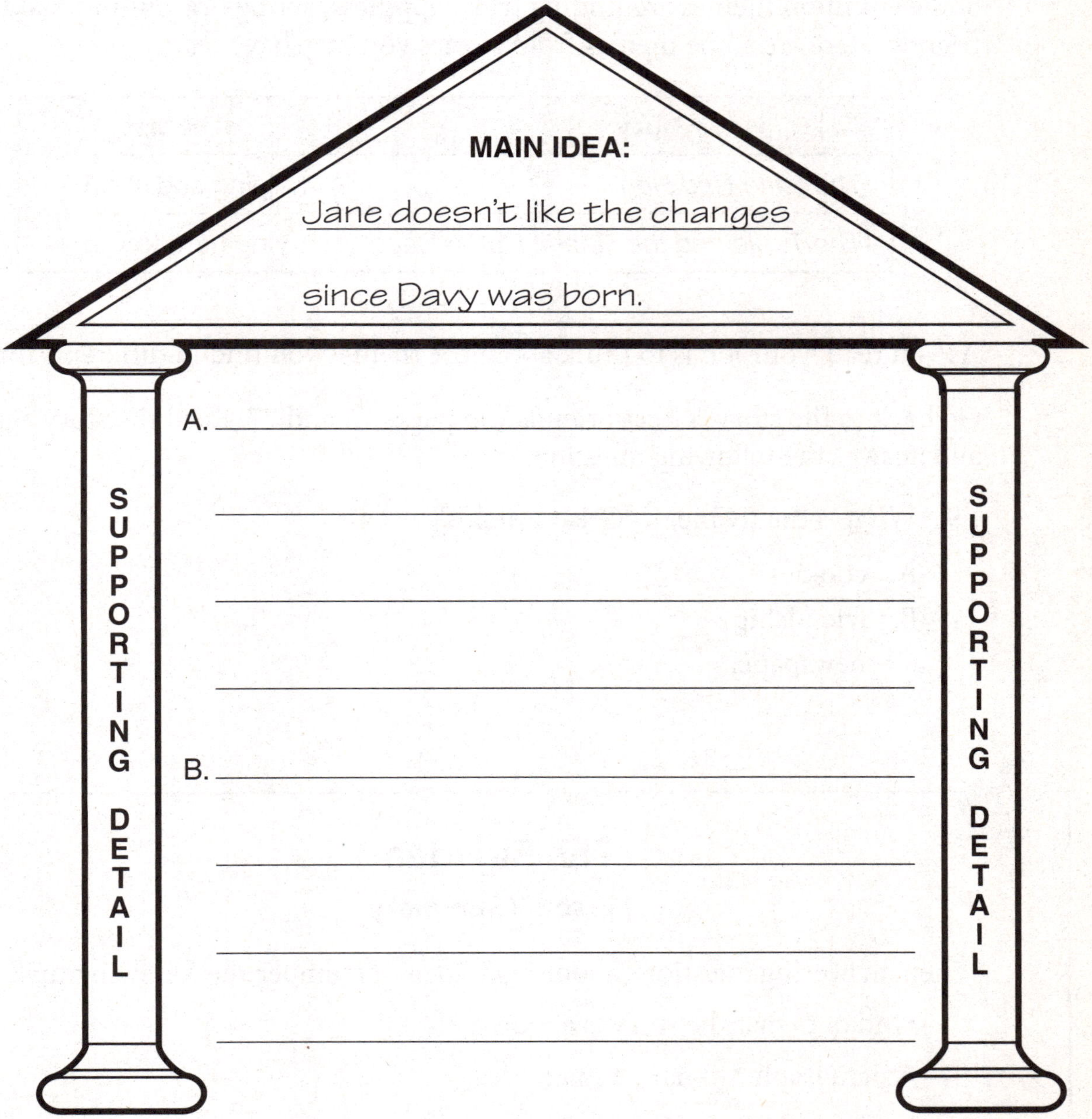

TIP 6: Understand the theme of the story.

The **theme** of a a story is bigger than the main idea. The theme connects a selection to real life. The theme of a story tells something about life or asks an important question.

Some common themes are finding true happiness, acting bravely and making friends. Here are some themes from stories you may have read.

Story	Theme
The Little Red Hen	helping and sharing
The Turtle and the Rabbit Run a Race	trying hard to win

As you read, your job is to think about the themes you find in different stories.

Go back to the story "Great Friends" on pages 76 and 77. Read the story again and answer the following question.

9. What is the theme of "Great Friends"?

   A. cookies
   B. friendship
   C. newspapers

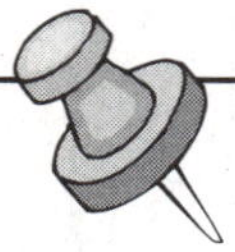

The Big Idea

Lesson 8 Summary

When answering questions about main idea, remember the following tips:

- Find out what the story is about.
- A paragraph can have a main idea.
- Look for the main idea sentence.
- Say the main idea in your own words.
- Details tell about the main idea.
- Understand the theme of the story.

Reading Achievement Practice begins on the following page.

Directions: Read the selection.

Sam and Kai

by Susan McCarty

Our school is small. When the new student showed up, everyone knew about him right away. His name was Kai, and he was from a place called Japan. When he talked, his words sounded different from ours. Some of the kids thought the way he talked sounded strange. They made fun of him. At lunch, no one sat with Kai. He looked sad, so I sat with him.

"Hi, Kai," I said. "My name is Sam. How do you like our school so far?"

"I like it," Kai said. "It's smaller than my school in Japan. That is nice because it's easy to remember everyone's name."

I nodded. "That's true," I said.

We talked for a while. Even though we were from different parts of the world, we both liked many of the same things. We both loved baseball. We talked about different teams in America and Japan. Kai said the best baseball team in Japan is the Seibu Lions. Then the bell rang.

"Thank you for sitting with me, Sam," said Kai. "You should come to a baseball game with me and my family. My dad loves American baseball. When we moved here, he got season tickets to see the Cincinnati Reds."

"I'd love to go to a game with you. Thanks, Kai!" I said. I was glad I sat with Kai. He was nice and funny. Also, he knew a lot about baseball. We would have a great time together!

Go to next page

Directions: Use the selection to answer questions 1 – 6.

1. This paragraph is from the selection.

   "Our school is small. When the new student showed up, everyone knew about him right away. His name was Kai, and he was from a place called Japan. When he talked, his words sounded different than ours. Some of the kids thought the way he talked sounded strange. They made fun of him. At lunch, no one sat with Kai. He looked sad, so I sat with him."

   What is the main idea of this paragraph?

   O A. The school is small.
   O B. Kai is new at school.
   O C. Japan is a place far away.

2. What do Sam and Kai both like?

   O A. baseball
   O B. basketball
   O C. swimming

Go to next page

3. This sentence is from the story.

"Kai said the **best** team in Japan is the Seibu Lions."

Which word means the same as **best**?

O A. saddest
O B. funny
O C. greatest

4. What does Kai ask Sam to do?

O A. tell him everyone's name
O B. sit with him at lunch
O C. go to a baseball game

5. What is the theme of this selection?

O A. lunchtime
O B. kindness
O C. baseball

Go to next page

6. What is this selection about?

____

____

List three details that support the main idea.

a. ____________________________________

____

b. ____________________________________

____

c. ____________________________________

____

Achievement Coverage: RP.C.4, RP.D.3

Lesson 9: Details

Do you know the story "Goldilocks and the Three Bears"? Could you retell the story if someone asked you to? Do you remember what Goldilocks did? Whose bed did Goldilocks fall asleep in?

You can answer all of these questions by looking at a story's details. In Lesson 8, you learned that details are important because they tell about what things look like, sound like, and so on. Details help explain the main idea of the story. They also make the story more fun to read.

This lesson will teach you many things about the details that support the main idea.

Two Charlies

by Juanita Kopaska

Charlie did not do very well in school. He was not good at sports. He was shy and afraid of girls.

But Charlie was good at one thing in school. He could draw pictures called cartoons. He was very proud of his drawings.

Charlie began selling some of his cartoons when he was about 25 years old.

When he was 28, Charlie began drawing a cartoon boy. This boy was a lot like Charlie himself. The cartoon boy did not do well in school. He was not very good at sports. He was shy. He was afraid of girls. And his name was Charlie, too.

The cartoon boy was Charlie Brown. There were other cartoon boys and girls, too. The story of these cartoon boys and girls was called *Peanuts*. Every week, there was a little cartoon story about Charlie Brown and his friends in the newspaper.

The man who drew Charlie Brown for over 50 years was Charles M. Schulz. "Charlie" is a nickname for "Charles." Mr. Schulz also created Lucy, Linus, Snoopy, and the rest of the *Peanuts* cartoon boys and girls.

Peanuts was read by people all over. It helped the two shy Charlies become known and loved around the world.

Achievement Coverage: RP.C.4, RP.D.3

Every story has a main idea. In "Two Charlies," the main idea is that the two Charlies were the same in many ways. We know that Charles Schulz and Charlie Brown were like each other because the story's details tell us so.

TIP 1: Details help you understand the main idea.

Details are the little pieces of information in a story. They help us understand the main idea. They help us answer questions about the main idea, too. In the story "Two Charlies," the details show how Charles Schulz and Charlie Brown were like each other.

1. When Charles Schulz was in school, what was he proud of?

   A. playing sports
   B. drawing cartoons
   C. being a good student

2. Who is Charlie Brown?

   A. a boy in a cartoon
   B. a boy who likes cartoons
   C. Charles Schulz's friend

3. What is the name of the cartoon stories Charles Schulz drew?

   A. *Snoopy*
   B. *Peanuts*
   C. *Charlie Brown*

TIP 2: A main idea web can help you remember a story.

A **main idea web** is a picture that shows you the main idea and details of a story. You can draw one to help you remember a story.

Here's a main idea web for "Two Charlies."

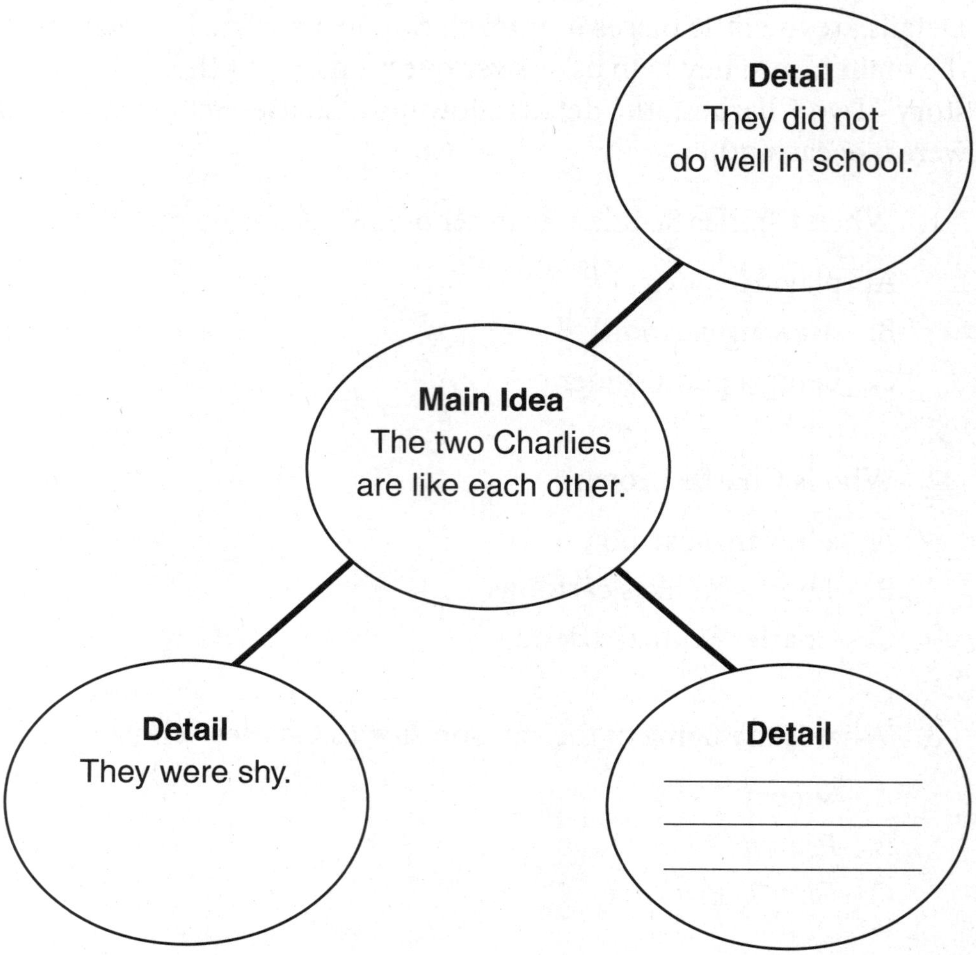
Detail
They did not do well in school.
Main Idea
The two Charlies are like each other.
Detail
They were shy.
Detail

4. Which detail can be added to the main idea web?

   A. They both drew cartoons.

   B. They were both proud.

   C. They were not good at sports.

Achievement Coverage: RP.C.4, RP.D.3

TIP 3: Details make pictures with words.

Details help you see the story in your mind.

Here is a sentence without many details:

I like being in this room.

What room is the sentence talking about? We just don't know. The sentence doesn't tell us. We need details to know more.

Here is a paragraph full of details about that room.

I like being in this room. The room has **a bed** and **a desk**. It also has **a clock, a telephone,** and **a television**.

Now we know more. We know what's in the room. We can begin to see it on our own.

Here's another paragraph that uses even more details. Use these details to help you draw a picture in your mind.

I like being in this **large room**. The room has a **soft** bed and a desk **with five drawers**. It also has a **yellow** clock, a **green** telephone, and a **big** television.

5. Now draw a picture of the room. Use crayons or colored pencils to show details from the paragraph.

Achievement Coverage: RP.C.4, RP.D.3

Details

Lesson 9 Summary

When answering questions about details, remember the following tips:

- Details help you understand the main idea.
- A main idea web can help you remember a story.
- Details make pictures with words.

Reading Achievement Practice begins on the following page.

Directions: Read the selection.

Bird or Cat?

Many fun animals live in Ohio. Some of them can be found in zoos or animal parks. If you look hard enough, you might find one right outside your door.

Maybe you have seen a gray catbird before. It has a funny name, but it looks like any other bird. It isn't very big. It doesn't have bright colors. It is small and gray, just like its name says. What makes this bird unusual? The catbird might look like a bird, but it sounds like a cat!

The gray catbird is a songbird. Songbirds like to sing. Songbirds also like trees. They sit on high branches and sing. This is how they talk to each other. They fill the air with their music. Catbirds are different. They don't always sing. Sometimes they meow just like a cat.

Catbirds don't sit in trees, either. Catbirds live in secret. Catbirds hide in bushes. This is where they build their nests and care for their babies. The bushes make it hard for other animals to see catbirds. This keeps them safe.

Catbirds also need warm weather to live. They stay in Ohio during the spring and summer. This is when it is warmest outside. They fly away in the fall. The catbirds come back when winter is over.

You don't have to go to the zoo to see a catbird. You can find this funny animal almost anywhere. Look at the ground instead of in trees. Look in summer, not winter. And make sure to keep your ears open.

The next time you hear a cat meowing outside, don't be so sure. It might be a catbird!

Go to next page

Directions: Use the selection to answer questions 1 – 7.

1. These sentences are from the selection.

   "What makes this bird **unusual**? The catbird might look like a bird, but it sounds like a cat!"

   What does **unusual** mean?

   O A. silly
   O B. pretty
   O C. different

2. How do songbirds talk to each other?

   O A. They sing.
   O B. They fly.
   O C. They sit.

3. Where do catbirds build their nests?

   O A. in trees
   O B. in bushes
   O C. in grass

Go to next page

4. When should you try to find a catbird?

   - O A. in summer
   - O B. in fall
   - O C. in winter

5. Which sentence is true about catbirds?

   - O A. Catbirds like to sing in trees.
   - O B. Catbirds are small and gray.
   - O C. Catbirds fly away in summer.

6. What could be another title for this reading selection?

   - O A. The Music of Birds
   - O B. Going to the Zoo
   - O C. One Funny Animal

Go to next page

7. Catbirds are different from other songbirds.

Give two examples of things that make them different.

a. ____

____

b. ____

____

STOP

Achievement Coverage: RP.E.6

Lesson 10: Asking Questions

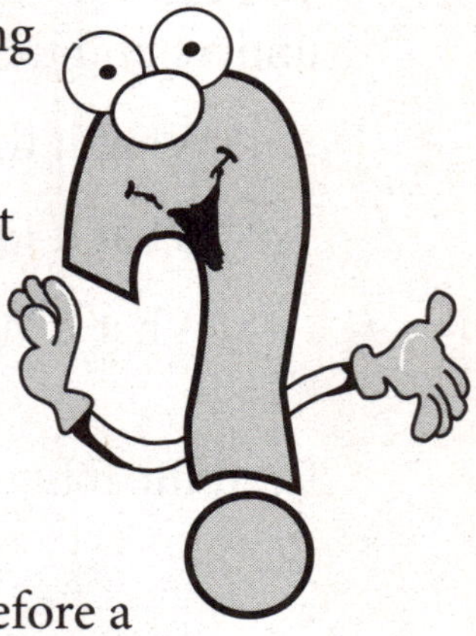

Do you ask questions when you read? It's a really good thing to do. There are lots of questions you can ask when you read. Questions can help you find important ideas and details in what you read. In this lesson, you will learn about some important questions you can ask.

TIP 1: Asking questions helps you find the details.

A reporter is a person who writes stories in newspapers. Before a reporter writes a story, she asks a lot of questions. The answers to these questions are the details. She'll put them in her story.

The Reporter's Questions

Who?

What?

When?

Where?

Why?

How?

You can ask these questions about true stories and about made-up stories. As you read, ask yourself these reporter's questions. Then look for the details that answer those questions.

TIP 2: Ask yourself "What if?" questions.

You can also ask yourself "What if?" questions. These questions will help you understand the things you read about. Here are three examples:

What if the little girl meets a wolf in the woods?

What if Joe moves to another city?

What if Wendy doesn't know how to swim?

Read the following newspaper story.

Circus will open in Gotham City on Friday

Ben Post is the ringmaster of the Bellwater Circus. He said today that the circus will open in Gotham City on Friday afternoon as planned.

Many people were afraid that the circus would not open until later next week. The show's lions and elephants went to Metropolis by mistake. Post said this happened because of a trucking mix-up.

"Our trucks are bringing the animals back to Gotham City right now," Post said. "Hang on to your tickets. The show will open on time."

Achievement Coverage: RP.E.6

Now write some questions that can be answered by the details in the story. We did the first question for you.

1. Write a "who?" question about the story.

   Who is the ringmaster of the Bellwater Circus?

2. Write a "why?" question about the story.

3. Write a "what if?" question about the story.

4. Write a "where?" question about the story.

5. Which of these "how?" questions is answered by the newspaper story?

   A. How did Ben Post get the job of ringmaster?
   B. How many people have tickets for the circus?
   C. How are the animals being moved to Gotham City?

6. Circle the drawing that best tells about the main idea of the newspaper story.

A.

B.

C.

Achievement Coverage: RP.E.6

TIP 3: Key words are signs that help you find the answers.

Key words are important words from the story. On a test, you must answer questions. Sometimes, a question that asks about details will have important words from the story in it. These key words are signs to help you find the answer to the question.

Most questions have at least one key word in them. Sometimes the answers also have key words. Look for key words in the story. They will help you find the correct answer.

Read the passage below:

> There were many people to tell that boy what to do. There was his mother and his father, his grandfather, and his older brother. And there was also an aunt, who was always saying: "Do this. Do that." Every day this aunt would shout at him and make a great noise that would frighten the birds.
>
> The boy did not like his aunt.
>
> —from "Strange Animals," *Children of Wax: African Folk Tales* by Alexander McCall Smith

Read the questions that follow. They are about the passage you just read. Some key words are printed in dark letters. Look for these key words in the passage. They will help you find the answers.

7. Who **tells** the boy **what to do**?

   A. many people
   B. only his aunt
   C. only his mother

8. Which word best tells about the boy's **brother**?

   A. bigger
   B. older
   C. stronger

9. What does the boy's **aunt** do that would **frighten the birds**?

   A. She throws things.
   B. She runs after the boy.
   C. She makes a great noise.

TIP 4: Think about what happens first.

Details help us put events in order. Sometimes detail questions will ask what happened first, next, or last.

Read the story below. As you read, picture the story in your mind. Picture what happens to Ely and his dog, Banjo. This will help you remember what happens first, next, and last in the story.

Flying Kites

by Pauline Stark

Ely decided to take his dog, Banjo, to the park on Saturday. The sun was shining. The sky was blue. It was a beautiful day for a walk in the park.

When they got to the park, Ely saw six different kites in the sky. They were all different shapes and colors. A bunch of different kids and adults were flying them.

One kite had a bright red ladybug on it. Another kite looked like a green dragon. There was one kite that was all different colors and looked like an empty box.

Ely was watching the kites when he felt the leash jerk out of his hand. Banjo was running away! Ely chased after him into the bushes. He found Banjo with a small kite in his jaws. "Where did you get that, boy?" Ely asked Banjo. A little girl came up to them.

"It's my kite. I was running to get it, and your dog chased me."

"I'm sorry," said Ely. "But he's a really friendly dog. He just thought you were playing." Ely patted Banjo on the head and the girl did the same.

On page 217, you will see four boxes. Inside each box is a picture. These pictures tell about the story you have just read. Carefully cut out the boxes and lay them on your desk.

Now we will use the pictures to retell the story.

10. Put the pictures in the same order as the story. Put the picture of the first thing that happens in Box 1. Then, put the picture of the second thing that happens in Box 2, and so on.

When your pictures are in the right order, glue them in the boxes on page 103.

Achievement Coverage: RP.A.5

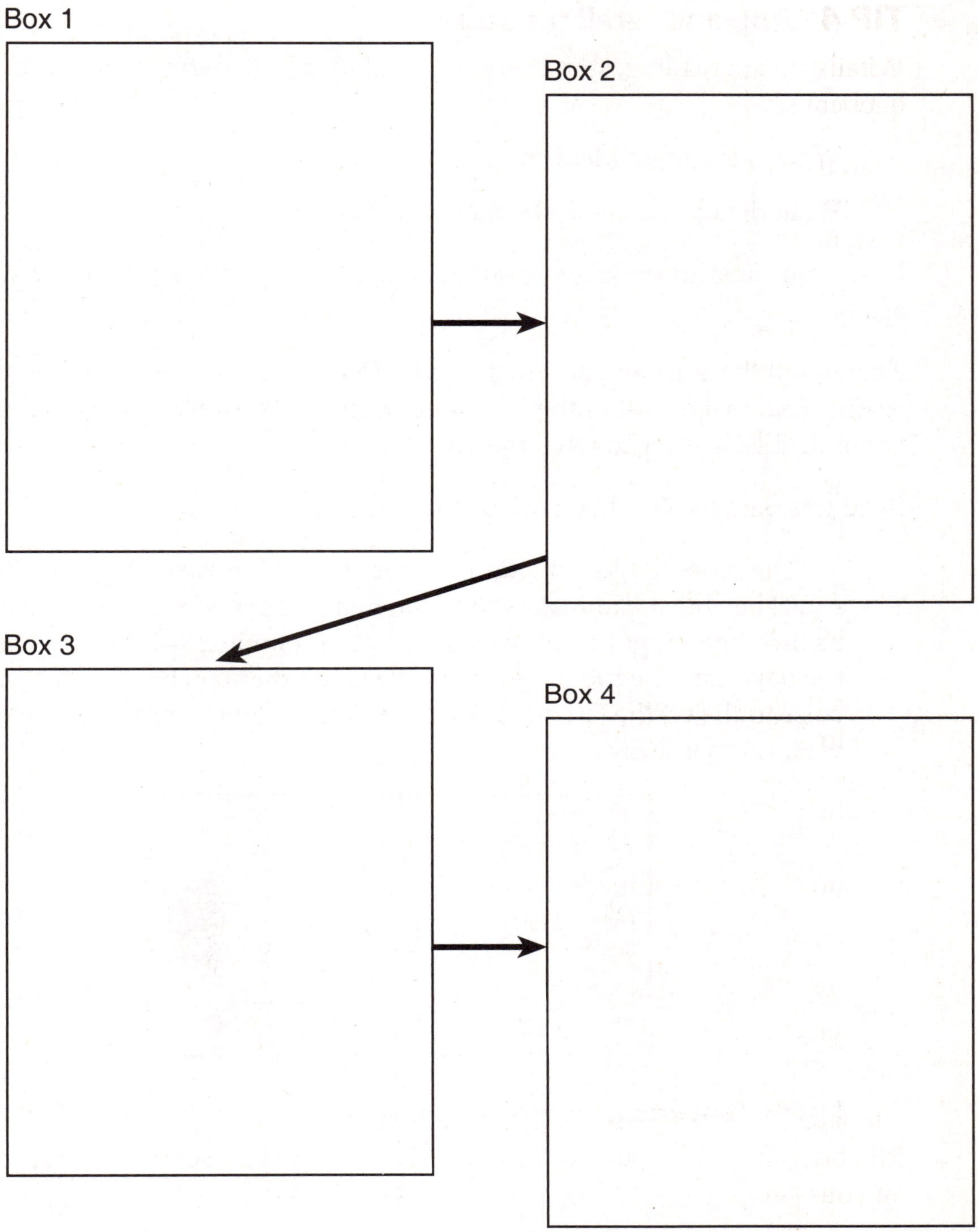

TIP 5: Stop and retell the story.

When you are reading, stop every now and then and ask yourself these questions:

What is the main idea?

What details tell about the main idea?

If you can't answer these questions, go back and read all or part of the story again.

Then retell the story in your own words. To **retell** a story means to tell the story again. First, make a list of the most important parts. Don't worry too much about details. Just try to retell the big ideas.

Read this paragraph. Then answer Number 11.

The moon looks brighter than the stars, but it isn't. Stars are like our sun. They burn and make their own light. The moon does not make its own light. Light from the sun hits the moon just as it hits the earth in the daytime. The moon looks brighter than the stars because it is very close to the earth. The stars don't look very bright to us because they are very, very far away.

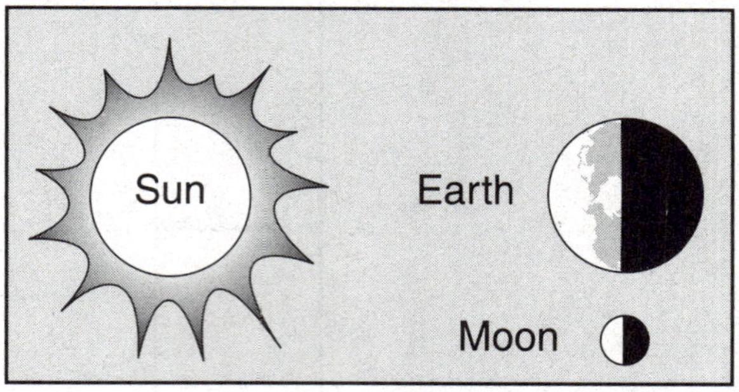

11. List two important parts of the paragraph.

____

____

____

____

____

____

Achievement Coverage: RP.F.7, RP.F.8

Asking Questions

Lesson 10 Summary

When answering questions about asking questions, remember the following tips:

- Asking questions helps you find the details.
- Ask yourself "What if?" questions.
- Key words are signs that help you find the answers.
- Think about what happens first.
- Stop and retell the story.

Reading Achievement Practice begins on the following page.

Directions: Read the selection.

Lori's Surprise

by Barbara L. Hauth

Amy called Lori to come over and play. Lori put on her skates. She skated down the sidewalk to Amy's house. At Amy's house, Lori found a note. Here is what it said:

> If you are Lori, go
> to Carlos's house.
> Love,
> Amy

Lori skated to Carlos's house. She rang the doorbell. Carlos's mother answered the door. "Hi, Lori," she said. "Carlos asked me to tell you to go to David's house."

At David's house, Lori saw a note on the mailbox. This is what it said:

> Lori,
> Go to the big tree
> by Justin's house. Be
> as quiet as a mouse.

Lori skated to Justin's house. She leaned against the big, old oak tree and listened.

Justin's voice said over and over, "Lori, please go to Keesha's house. Lori, please go to Keesha's house. Lori, please go to Keesha's house." The voice came from a small tape recorder in the hollow of the tree.

Lori skated up to Keesha's front door.

"Oh, good," Lori said. "This time there's no note." Keesha's mother opened the door. She asked Lori to come in.

Soon, balloons, horns, flowers, and five faces appeared around the corner. "Surprise! Happy birthday, Lori!" All of Lori's friends were there and wearing birthday hats.

Lori was very surprised. "My birthday isn't until next week!"

"We know," said Keesha. "We wanted to surprise you. So we're having your party today."

Lori smiled a great big smile. It was fun to have such wonderful friends.

Go to next page

Directions: Use the selection to answer questions 1 – 7.

1. Number the events in Lori's day in the order that they happen.

   ____ Lori leans on a big, old oak tree.

   ____ Amy calls Lori to come over and play.

   ____ Keesha's mother opens the front door.

2. How does Lori go from house to house?

   O A. on a bicycle

   O B. on a skateboard

   O C. on skates

3. What does Lori find at Justin's house?

   O A. a note on the mailbox

   O B. a tape recorder with a message

   O C. balloons, horns, and her friends

4. Where does Lori finally get her surprise?

   O A. at David's house

   O B. at Lori's house

   O C. at Keesha's house

Go to next page

5. Choose the answer that completes the web below.

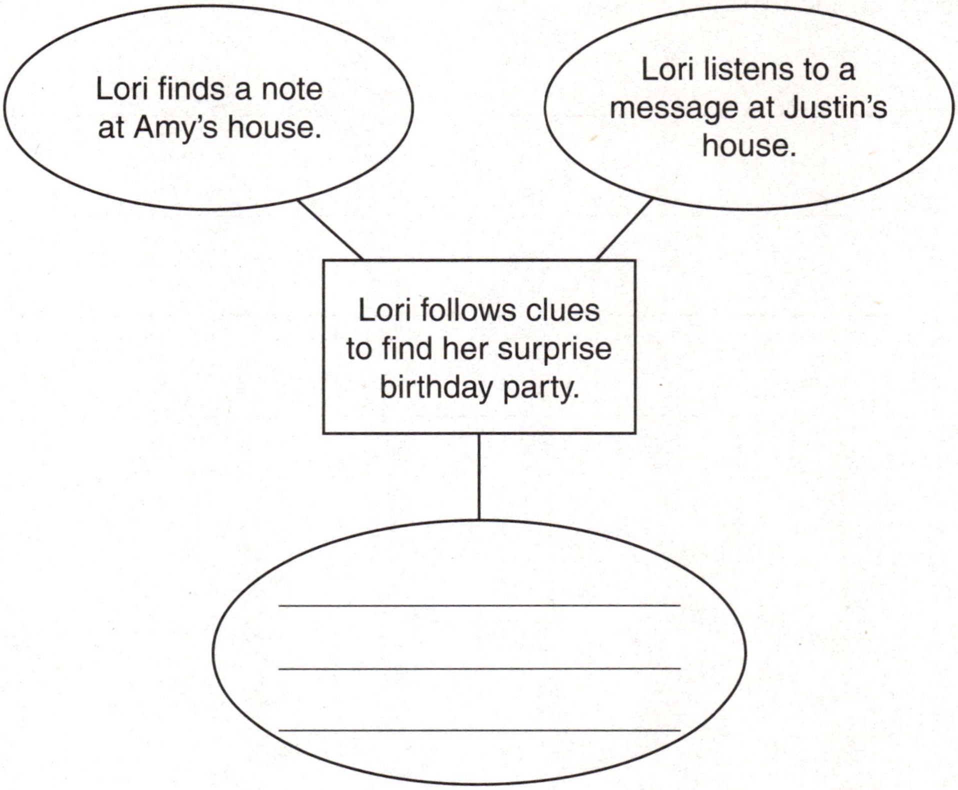
Lori finds a note at Amy's house.
Lori listens to a message at Justin's house.
Lori follows clues to find her surprise birthday party.

- ○ A. Carlos's mother tells Lori to go to David's house.
- ○ B. Keesha likes to write notes for Lori to find.
- ○ C. Lori uses skates because her bicycle is broken.

6. Which of these words is in the same word family as the word **house**?

- ○ A. skates
- ○ B. horns
- ○ C. mouse

7. Use the information in the selection to list two things that Lori sees at her party.

a. ____

____

b. ____

____

STOP

Achievement Coverage: RP.B.2

Lesson 11: Putting Details Together

In made-up stories, there is always some kind of big problem. There may be many smaller problems, too.

Sometimes, the writer tells you exactly what the main problem is. Most of the time, you have to find out the main problem by yourself. You do this by putting together details.

Read the following story.

Mouse Trouble

by Rafael Rogers

It was a morning like any other morning. Julie sat at the table eating her breakfast. Her mom was getting ready for work.

Julie sat at the table. She looked out the door of the kitchen. Their back door was all glass. She watched the birds flying around. Then she saw her cat, Tabby, at the door.

Julie got up and let him in without looking at him. Just as Julie was closing the door, her mom walked into the kitchen.

"Julie!" she said. "Why did you let Tabby in the house? He has a mouse!" Julie's mom tried to grab Tabby. Just as she got near him, Tabby set the mouse on the floor. The mouse ran across the kitchen. Julie jumped and bumped the table. Her cup fell on the floor. Tabby ran right through the milk as he was chasing the mouse.

Tabby ran across Julie's schoolbag, getting it all full of milk. Then the mouse ran right over Julie's mom's feet! Her mom screamed! Then it turned around and ran right under Julie! As the mouse ran to the living room, Tabby ran after the mouse. Julie's mom ran after Tabby. Julie didn't know what to do. So she ran after her mom to see what would happen.

The mouse ran into the living room and behind a chair. Tabby was trying to get behind the chair, too. Julie's mom pushed the chair out of the way so they could see where the mouse was. But the mouse was gone. Tabby kept poking his paw at the wall. They moved him out of the way. They saw a tiny hole in the wall. The mouse had found a way out.

Julie's mom let out a deep breath. "Well we better start cleaning up this mess," she said. Julie looked around. There were milk footprints all over the room. Then she remembered there was still milk all over the kitchen floor. Julie thought her mom was mad, but then she saw her mom smile. Julie went back to the kitchen to start cleaning.

Julie's mom was glad the mouse was gone. So was Julie. But Tabby looked mad. He wanted to play with the mouse some more. But Julie thought the mouse was probably pretty happy after all. Now all Julie had to do was help her mom clean up and get to school on time.

In the story you just read, Julie is eating her breakfast. When she sees Tabby at the door, she lets him in. Julie doesn't look at Tabby to see if he has anything in his mouth. This is the start of the problems. This helps make a bigger problem.

1. Read the story again and draw a line under some of the problems.

2. What is the main problem in the story?

   A. The house is a mess.

   B. Tabby catches a mouse.

   C. Julie has to clean up.

Achievement Coverage: RP.B.2

TIP 1: Retelling the story will help you understand it.

The **events** in a story are the things that happen. Retelling a story's events in order will help you understand it.

Events in a story are like the numbers in a dot-to-dot drawing. You have to put your pencil at dot number 1 to draw a line to dot number 2. In a story, the first event (1) has to happen before the second event (2) can happen.

Here's a dot-to-dot picture for you to finish. It will show something from the story "Mouse Trouble."

3. With your pencil, connect the dots in order from 1 to 18.

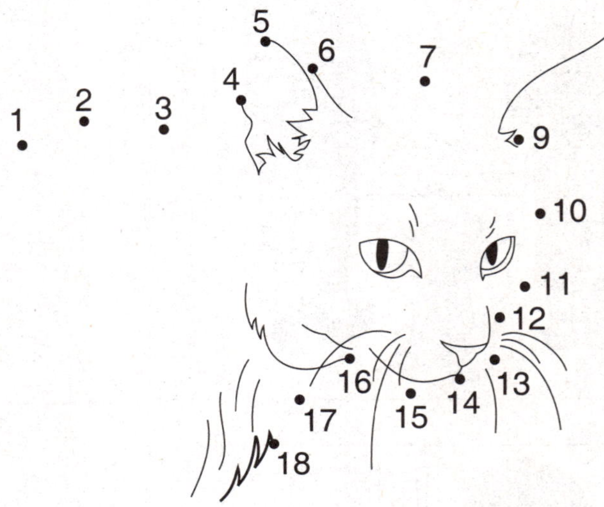

4. Put these story events in order by numbering the boxes from 1 to 4.

____

____

____

____

Achievement Coverage: RP.B.2

5. Think of a story you know well. This story might be “Little Red Riding Hood,” “The Three Little Pigs,” or another story. Write what happens in the story on the lines below.

Achievement Coverage: RP.B.2

TIP 2: One event makes another event happen.

Most of the time, one event in a story causes another event. To **cause** something means to make something happen.

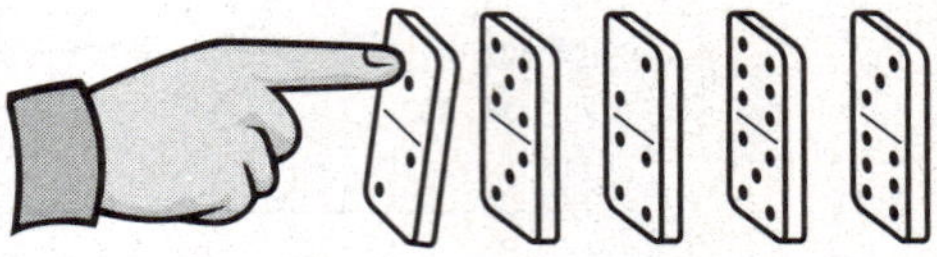

Think about dominos. Steve sets up a row of dominos. He pushes the first domino and it falls. Steve makes the domino fall. He is the cause.

The first domino makes the second domino fall. The first domino causes the second domino to fall.

Think back to the story "Mouse Trouble." In that story, there is a reason why the house gets messy.

6. Look back at the story. Draw a line under the sentence or sentences that tell what makes the house messy.

7. Why does Julie's house get messy?

   A. Julie is eating breakfast before school.

   B. The cat wants to come into the house.

   C. Tabby lets a mouse go in the house.

TIP 3: You can put events together by making a "because" sentence.

You can put events together by making a "because" sentence. The word *because* can show how one event causes another.

Julie lets Tabby in the house *because* she doesn't see that he has a mouse.

Julie's milk spills *because* Julie bumps into the table.

8. Finish this "because" sentence about the story.

   The mouse runs around the house because

   ____

   ____

   ____

   ____.

Achievement Coverage: RP.B.2, RP.D.3

TIP 4: The solution is how a problem is fixed.

The **solution** is how a problem is fixed. To **solve** a problem means to fix the problem. Sometimes the writer tells you about the solution. Sometimes you have to guess how the problem will be fixed. The story's details will help you.

9. Look back at the story. Draw a box around any sentences that tell you how Julie and her mom will solve the problem of the messy house.

10. How will Julie and her mom solve the problem of the messy house?

____

____

____

____

TIP 5: Think about the story and your own life.

Sometimes it helps to ask yourself if the story makes you think of something in your own life. This can help you understand how the people in the story feel.

11. Do the details of the story "Mouse Trouble" make you think of something that has happened in your own life? Write about a time someone or something made a mess.

____

____

____

____

12. How is your story the same as "Mouse Trouble"?

____

____

____

13. How is your story different from "Mouse Trouble"?

____

____

____

Putting Details Together

Lesson 11 Summary

When answering questions about putting details together, remember the following tips:

- Retelling the story will help you understand it.
- One event makes another event happen.
- You can put events together by making a "because" sentence.
- The solution is how a problem is fixed.
- Think about the story and your own life.

Reading Achievement Practice begins on the following page.

Directions: Read the selection.

The Wrong Bus

Robert Nord

It was the first day of school. Jody stood at the end of his street. He was waiting for the bus. Jody had never taken the bus before. His mom had always taken him to school. But over the summer, his mom got a new job. She had to be at work earlier than before. She couldn't take Jody to school anymore. That was okay with Jody because he thought the bus might be fun. Who would be on it? Would he make new friends on the bus? After a while, he began to worry. Where was the bus? It seemed like he'd been standing outside for a long time.

Finally, a school bus pulled up. His heart beat a little harder as he climbed up the stairs. He got to the top of the stairs and began to walk toward the back. As he walked, he looked at some of the kids on the bus. They looked older than Jody . . . a lot older. Oh no! He must have gotten on the high school bus. He ran back up to the front to tell the driver, but the bus had already pulled away.

"Wait, I'm on the wrong bus!" Jody said to the driver.

"Well, that's a problem," said the driver. "What do you want me to do?"

Jody thought for a moment. He couldn't stay on the bus. What would he do at the high school all day? His mom couldn't come pick him up because she was at work. And he didn't want to miss the first day of school. He looked out the window at the rows of houses as they passed. They looked like little boxes in all different colors. He'd seen those boxes before! He watched out the window a little longer until he found the house he was looking for. It was Jason's house! His mom had driven him here many times. Farther down the street, Jody saw Jason standing at the corner. He was waiting for the bus to the elementary school.

"Let me off here. It's my friend's bus stop! I'll get on the right bus with him."

"Good idea," said the bus driver. "I'm glad you know what to do." He pulled the bus to the side of the road. Jody got off the bus. Boy was he glad to see Jason!

Directions: Use the selection to answer questions 1 – 7.

1. What happens first in the story?

   O A. Jody sees Jason's house.

   O B. Jody gets on the wrong bus.

   O C. Jody waits for the bus.

Go to next page

2. What is Jody's main problem?

O A. Jody is on the high school bus.

O B. Jody has to go to school.

O C. Jody's mom gets a new job.

3. Why does Jody take the bus?

O A. He wants to see what taking the bus is like.

O B. Jason also takes the bus to school.

O C. Jody's mom has to be at work earlier.

4. What are the boxes Jody sees from the bus?

O A. dogs

O B. houses

O C. toys

5. Why does Jody tell the driver to let him get off the bus?

O A. Jody is afraid of the kids on the bus.

O B. Jody sees his friend waiting for the bus.

O C. Jody is near where his mom works.

Go to next page

6. How will Jody solve his problem?

- O A. He will take the right bus with Jason.
- O B. He will call his mom from the high school.
- O C. He will not go to school on the first day.

7. Jody cares about getting to his elementary school. How can you tell? Give two examples of things that Jody says or does that show he cares.

a. ______________________________

b. ______________________________

STOP

Unit 4

Reading to Know

Have you ever been stumped by a really hard question? Where did you look to find the answer? Books are a great place to find information, but there are so many books in the world that it might be hard to know where to start. Reading is easier and more fun if you know why you are reading and what you expect to find out.

In this unit, you will learn about reading to find information. You will ask questions about writers. You will learn things to do before, during, and after reading. You will even learn how to read pictures. If you follow the tips in this unit, you'll never be stumped for long!

In This Unit

Lesson 12: The Writer's Clues

Reading is like playing detective. A **detective** is someone who finds the answers to mysteries. You have to take the writer's clues and put them together. If you do a good job, you will soon know the story.

TIP 1: Find the writer's purpose for writing.

A **purpose** is why someone does something. Writers can have different purposes for writing. Sometimes they want to teach us about something. Sometimes they want to help us have fun. And sometimes they want us to do something. They may want us to buy a certain kind of ice cream or go to a certain movie.

1. What other things might a writer want to make us do?

____

____

____

Finding the main idea of a story will help you understand the writer's reason for writing. Look for the main idea in the following passage.

Fun Facts About Ohio

by Lloyd Boyer

"Beautiful Ohio" is a good name for a state song. You can see many pretty trees and parks in Ohio. The most famous tree in Ohio is called the buckeye. Buckeye is both Ohio's state nickname and the state tree. The buckeye seed looks the eye of a deer. When you spot a buckeye, it seems like it is looking right back at you.

Ohio also has lots of beautiful buildings to see. Newark, Ohio, is the home of the Longaberger Basket Company. At seven floors high, the Longaberger building is the world's tallest building shaped like a picnic basket. Once inside, you can look up to see the huge basket handles high above your head. They are easy to see because the Longaberger's roof is made of glass.

If you are basket crazy, take a trip to Frazeysburg, Ohio. There you'll find the World's Largest Apple Basket. Each apple in the basket is the size of a third-grader. The whole basket stands almost 30-feet high. That is almost as tall as a traffic light!

There is no state in the country quite like Ohio. I think the best place to visit in Ohio is the city of Columbus. This is where Capitol Square is found. Very important laws are made right here in the Ohio Statehouse. The Ohio Statehouse is sometimes called the People's House because the people of Ohio are the ones elected to make the laws.

There are many other things to learn about Ohio. But the best way to learn about Ohio is to live there! You will love it, I promise. If you live in Ohio, be sure to visit some of the places that make the Buckeye State great.

2. What is the main idea of "Fun Facts About Ohio"?

   A. The Longaberger building is in Newark, Ohio.

   B. Ohio is called the Buckeye State.

   C. There are many things to learn about Ohio.

The writer of "Fun Facts About Ohio" is trying to teach his readers about Ohio. He also wants them to do something. Look at the end of the passage to find out what he wants his readers to do.

3. What does the writer of "Fun Facts About Ohio" want his readers to do?

   ____

   ____

   ____

Writers give other clues in their writing. The tips that follow will help you learn about these clues.

Directions: Read the story. It will help you with this lesson.

Mrs. Bagworthy

by Tiffany Carlisle

Mrs. Bagworthy did not like being in a box! She had lived in the sunny window of Thompson's Toy Store all her life. She liked sitting in her tiny red rocking chair and watching the people go by. She liked watching the busy little train that went around and around on a small circle of track by her feet. Most of all, Mrs. Bagworthy enjoyed watching the children who stopped to look at the toys in the window.

Every Saturday, a little girl with a crooked little smile pressed her nose against the window. The little girl wished she had a chubby, gray-haired doll like Mrs. Bagworthy.

"It would be so nice to go home with that little girl," Mrs. Bagworthy would say to herself.

One Saturday, Mrs. Bagworthy watched and waited. But the little girl with the crooked little smile did not come.

Then it happened!

Mr. Thompson snatched Mrs. Bagworthy from the window and taped her into a tight-fitting box.

"What's going on? What's happening?" Mrs. Bagworthy cried from inside her dark, cardboard package.

There was no answer.

Mr. Thompson finished wrapping the box in brown paper. He tossed it into a canvas mail bag.

Mrs. Bagworthy spent that night and part of the next day standing on her head. She was upside down in a mountain of packages at the post office.

Finally, a mail carrier put Mrs. Bagworthy into a truck. He took her to a small house.

Mrs. Bagworthy lay very still in her dark box. She could not see the sick child in bed. But she did hear a tiny voice say, "Oh, Papa, I hate being sick. And I miss seeing my friends. I'm so lonely."

"Here, little one," said a man with a soft voice. "I have a surprise for you. Now, you won't be so lonely."

He tore off the brown paper and carefully opened the box. He gently pulled out Mrs. Bagworthy. Then he placed the doll into the arms of his daughter. It was the little girl with a crooked little smile.

Achievement Coverage: RP.A.1, IT.B.3

TIP 2: Look for clues while you read.

Stories don't always tell you everything. Sometimes writers want you to think for yourself. They help you think by giving clues. They do this to get you interested in the story.

"Mrs. Bagworthy" doesn't tell everything about the characters. But the writer gives hints. These hints are in the details.

Think about the story. Why do you think the little girl stops coming to the toy store?

The writer doesn't tell us, but the story gives us a clue:

> "Mrs. Bagworthy lay very still in her dark box. She could not see *the sick child in bed*."

We know that *the little girl has stopped visiting the toy store.* We also know that *she is sick*. If we put these two details together, we know WHY the little girl has stopped visiting the store.

4. Why does the little girl stop visiting the toy store?

____

____

____

5. Cut out the jigsaw puzzle pieces on page 219. Put the pieces together to make a picture of Mrs. Bagworthy. Fit the pieces inside the box below. When you are sure all the pieces are in their correct places, glue them down one at a time.

TIP 3: Look for hidden messages in a story.

Finding hidden messages in a story is like solving a mystery. Sure, a writer could tell you everything. But you can think for yourself! You can come up with your own ideas.

Think about the story again. How do you think Mrs. Bagworthy will feel about living with the little girl?

To answer this question, look for clues in the story. Here are some of those clues:

- Mrs. Bagworthy enjoys children.
- Mrs. Bagworthy says, "It would be so nice to go home with that little girl."

6. How do you think Mrs. Bagworthy will feel about living with the little girl?

____

____

____

7. Pretend you are the little girl. You want to give Mrs. Bagworthy a new name. What name would you choose?

____

Why would you choose that name?

____

____

Achievement Coverage: RP.A.1, IT.B.3

8. Draw a picture of the little girl and Mrs. Bagworthy at the end of the story. Be sure your picture shows how the little girl feels. Look back at the story to help you.

The Writer's Clues

Lesson 12 Summary

When answering questions about the clues that writers leave behind, remember the following tips:

- Find the writer's purpose for writing.
- Look for clues while you read.
- Look for hidden messages in a story.

Reading Achievement Practice begins on the following page.

Directions: Read the selection.

Sam Saves the Day

by Steven Otfinoski

Tony had a pet goat. His name was Sam. He was white and had two big horns on his head.

He was pretty good-looking for a goat. Tony thought Sam was the best goat that ever lived. But not everyone did.

"A goat is no pet for a boy," said Tony's father. "It's crazy having a goat for a pet."

"A goat is a bad animal to have around children," said Tony's mother. "It might hurt them with its horns."

Tony didn't listen to them. "Sam's a good goat," he said. "And he's mine. That's all I care about."

Go to next page

Every day after school, Tony would go see his pet behind the house. He would bring Sam food. Then Tony would take Sam for a walk.

The other kids laughed when they saw Tony and his goat coming down the street. "How's Snow White today, Tony?" they asked.

Tony didn't stop. He went right on walking. He didn't want to get into a fight over Sam.

But one night at dinner, Tony's father said that Sam would have to go.

"I know how much you like that goat, Tony," said his father. "But it just does not look right having a goat in back of the house."

Tony's face turned red. He got up from the table and went over to his mother.

"Please, Mom," he said. "Let me keep Sam. I'll keep him out of everyone's way. You won't even know he's here."

"No, Tony," she said. "Your father's right. Sam must go tomorrow morning. A farmer is coming to take him away. He'll be happy in his new home."

Tony's father put his hand on Tony's arm. "You can get another pet," he said. "What about a dog?"

Tony looked like he was going to cry. "I don't want a dog," he said, running out of the room.

That night, it rained very hard. Tony took Sam into the basement. "I'm not going to let you get wet on your last night here," he said.

"Maaaaaaa," said Sam. He sounded pleased.

Go to next page

Tony sat down in the cold basement next to Sam and went to sleep. He jumped at the sound of a window opening. Someone was coming into the basement!

Tony didn't make a sound. He could hear two men talking in the dark. "Come on, Harry. Let's go up into the house," said one of them.

"I hope they have good things to take, Joe," said the other man.

Tony didn't know what to do. Just then Sam got up.

"Maaaaaaa!"

"Did you say something?" asked Harry.

"No," said Joe. "I heard it, too."

"Maaaaaaa!"

"There it is again," said Joe. "It sounds like an animal."

"We'd better take a look," said Harry.

Harry turned on a light. "What do you know!" he cried. "An old billy goat."

"He isn't old," said Tony, standing up. "And you get out of here!"

"Sure, man," said Joe, "just as soon as we get what we came for."

Joe came at Tony with his two hands.

"MAAAAAAA!"

"Shut that goat up," Joe said to Harry, "before he gets everyone up!"

Go to next page

Sam didn't like the two men. He put his head down and started running at Harry. Harry took one look at those horns and ran.

"Let me go!" cried Tony as Joe went after him.

Sam ran right at Joe's back. He hit him so hard that Joe fell down. Joe got up and jumped out the window after Harry.

"Let's get out of here," he said. "That goat's too much for us!"

Tony's father and mother came running down to the basement.

"What's going on down here?" asked his mother.

"Sam just ran two men out of here," said Tony. "They wanted to take all our things."

Tony's mother looked at his father. "Well," his father said, "I guess we can't get along without a goat, after all!"

"Then I can keep Sam?" said Tony.

"I don't see why not," said his mother.

"Maaaaaaa," said Sam. And he meant it, too.

Directions: Use the selection to answer questions 1 – 7.

1. Why does Tony's mother think it is bad to have a goat around children?

   ○ A. A goat might step on children.

   ○ B. A goat might chew children's clothing.

   ○ C. A goat might hurt children with its horns.

Go to next page

2. When the other kids say, "How's Snow White today, Tony?" who are they are talking about?

   - O A. Joe
   - O B. Sam
   - O C. Harry

3. Why does Tony's face turns red at the dinner table?

   - O A. He is angry.
   - O B. He is feeling sick.
   - O C. He is choking.

4. What happens after Harry runs away?

   - O A. Sam hits Joe with his horns.
   - O B. Sam jumps out the window after Harry.
   - O C. Tony's father runs after Joe.

5. At the end of the story, how does Mother feel about Tony keeping Sam?

   - O A. tired
   - O B. happy
   - O C. sad

Go to next page

6. What is the purpose of this selection?

   - O A. show readers that goats make great pets
   - O B. teach readers how to take care of a goat
   - O C. tell readers a story about a boy and his pet goat

7. What does Harry mean when he says, "I hope they have good things to take, Joe"?

   ____

   ____

   Support your answer with three examples from the reading selection.

   1. ____

      ____

   2. ____

      ____

   3. ____

      ____

STOP

Achievement Coverage: IT.A.1

Lesson 13: Road Signs for Reading

When you have questions, books are great places to find answers. This unit will help you use the "road signs for reading" to find important information in books.

Directions: Read the following selection. Use it to help you through this lesson.

Jason Gets a Fish

Jason told his sister, Melissa, "Mom and Dad said I could have a fish tank. Now I have to think about what kind of fish I want to put in it."

"We can go to the school library," Melissa said. "The library has books about fish and how to take care of them." When Jason and Melissa went to the library, they looked for books about fish. They found lots of books with the word *fish* in the title. "I can't read all of these books!" Jason said. "I just want a book that will tell me about caring for pet fish."

Melissa said, "You can tell which book to choose by reading the titles. Titles are like road signs that point you in the right direction."

TIP 1: Find the right title.

When Jason and Melissa went to the library, they looked for books about fish. They found lots of books with the word *fish* in the title.

Directions: Look at this list of titles to help Jason find the right book.

Ohio's Best Fishing Spots

Taking Care of Pet Fish

Space Fish from Planet X

Justin's Fish and Seafood Cookbook

The Great Book of Ocean Fish

Fish of North America

Some of these titles look like the names of storybooks. Others seem to be about fish that live in the ocean.

1. Which book would teach Jason about raising fish in a fish tank?

____

____

One of these titles looks like the name of a storybook. Another seems to be about how to cook fish. Only one of these books will have the information Jason wants.

2. Which book would tell how to cook fish?

    A. *Ohio's Best Fishing Spots*
    B. *Taking Care of Pet Fish*
    C. *Justin's Fish and Seafood Cookbook*

3. Which book is most likely a made-up story?

    A. *Space Fish from Planet X*
    B. *The Great Book of Ocean Fish*
    C. *Fish of North America*

Achievement Coverage: IT.A.1

TIP 2: Search the book using the table of contents.

You already know that the title helps you know what a book is about.

A **table of contents** gives a page number for each part of the book. It is found near the front of most books.

Chapters are parts that make up a book. Each chapter tells part of the book's story or gives part of the book's information.

Let's read more about Jason and Melissa.

> Jason and Melissa found many books about fish. They picked one book that looked very good. That book was *Taking Care of Pet Fish* by Alice Smith. Jason and Melissa opened the book to its table of contents.

This is what the table of contents looked like:

Table of Contents

Help Jason find the information he needs by answering these questions about the table of contents.

4. Jason isn't sure about what kind of fish he wants. On which page can he find help?

   A. 5

   B. 13

   C. 17

5. Jason wants to find out what it will be like to have his own fish. To which page should he turn?

   A. 5
   B. 13
   C. 24

6. Which chapter should Jason read to find out what his fish will eat?

   A. Choosing Your Fish
   B. Feeding Your Fish
   C. Cleaning Your Fish Tank

7. What chapter heading would Jason find at the top of page 24?

   A. Having Fish of Your Own
   B. Feeding Your Fish
   C. Cleaning Your Fish Tank

Road Signs for Reading

Lesson 13 Summary

When answering questions about parts of a book, remember the following tips:

- Find the right title.
- Search the book using the table of contents.

Reading Achievement Practice begins on the following page.

Directions: Read the selection.

Sara lives in Ottawa, Ohio. Over the winter, Sara saw a beaver, a raccoon and a red fox in her yard. She decided to go to the library to find out more about animals that live in Ohio. Here are some of the books Sara found:

Directions: Use the selection to answer questions 1 – 5.

1. Which book would tell Sara the **most** about all the different animals that live in Ohio?

   O A. Animals of Ohio

   O B. Fishing in Ohio

   O C. All About Ohio's Insects

Directions: Use the table of contents from a book about animals below to answer questions 2 – 3.

Table of Contents

2. Where would you find out more information about beavers, raccoons and red foxes living in Ohio?

   O A. 3
   O B. 9
   O C. 17

3. Where would you find out the most information about robins in Ohio?

   O A. 3
   O B. 9
   O C. 17

Go to next page

4. Which of these books will probably have information about the different bugs in Ohio?

O A. *Fishing in the Ohio*

O B. *All About Ohio's Insects*

O C. *Cougar and Rabbit Visit Ohio*

5. Which word has the same sound as the underlined letters in **beaver**?

O A. catch

O B. pen

O C. seed

6. Which word has the same sound as the underlined letters in **raccoon**?

O A. blue

O B. cloud

O C. sleep

Lesson 14: Tell Me a True Story

Sometimes it is fun to read about real people, real places and real events. You can learn a lot when you read about a real person's life, a special place or something that really happened.

True stories are not made up. Many of the stories you read in school are true stories. Newspaper stories are also true. In this lesson you will learn about true stories.

TIP 1: True stories tell about real things and real people.

The story of *Jack and the Beanstalk* is made up. A story that tells about how to plant beans is a story about real things.

A book about monsters from space is made up. A book that tells how to study the stars is about a real thing.

Remember, if a story tells facts about real things and people, it is not made up.

1. Which of these books is about a real thing?

   A. *Tony the Singing Goldfish*

   B. *How to Fly a Model Airplane*

   C. *The Ghost and the Magic Castle*

2. Which of the following is probably a made-up story?

   A. *All About Ohio's Lakes and Rivers*

   B. *Fun Games to Play After School*

   C. *The Monkey That Lives in My Hat*

TIP 2: True stories have facts that can be checked.

A **fact** is information that can be checked to see if it is right or wrong. Here are two fact sentences:

> Bicycles have two wheels.
>
> Mrs. Garcia teaches second grade.

You can check each of the facts above. You can count the number of wheels on a bicycle. You can ask Mrs. Garcia if she teaches second grade. Everybody can check these facts to see if they are right or wrong.

Newspaper stories are full of facts. Let's look at the kinds of things you could read about in a newspaper.

> City Swimming Pool to close for repairs.
>
> A new *Shrek* movie will open Saturday.
>
> School begins September 3.

These facts can be checked to see if they are right. You can ask somebody, or go to the pool, the movie, or your school to check it out for yourself.

3. Now, think of another fact you might read about in a newspaper. Remember that it has to be something that every reader could check. Write your fact sentence on the lines below.

   ____

   ____

   ____

TIP 3: Some true stories have opinions.

An **opinion** tells how someone feels about something. An opinion cannot be checked to see if it is right or wrong. Different people can have different feelings about the same thing.

Sometimes one word in a sentence will tell us it is an opinion. An opinion word means something different to every person.

Look at some examples.

best	strong
easy	fast
nice	

What does *fast* mean to you? A deer may be fast when compared to a turtle. A turtle may be fast when compared to a snail. *Fast* means different things to different people.

Most ads you see on TV or read in a newspaper are filled with opinion words.

4. Draw a line under the opinion word in this sentence from a newspaper ad.

   Cold Cow ice cream bars are the best snack ever.

The ad writer thinks Cold Cow ice cream bars are the best snack ever. But not everyone may think so. Some people may think Jack Frost ice cream bars are the best. Some people may think tuna-ripple ice cream cones are the best. The word *best* tells us that the sentence is an opinion.

5. Draw a line under the opinion word in this sentence.

   Making your own bicycle is easy with Big Bob's Bike Kit.

Do you think making a bicycle would be easy? Some people might find it hard. Words like *hard* and *easy* are opinion words.

6. Which of these sentences is an opinion?

   A. My dog is brown.
   B. My dog is wonderful.
   C. My dog is two years old.

Achievement Coverage: IT.C.4

TIP 4: Some true stories tell about real people.

"Class, it's time to go to the library," said Mrs. Green. "Each of you should find a book about a famous person."

Ty wanted to read about George Washington. He looked on the first shelf by the library door. He could not find a book about George Washington there. "Where should I look?" Ty asked.

The library helper said, "All books about famous people are in the same place." She took Ty to a shelf in the back.

"Here they are," Ty said, reaching for a book with George Washington's picture on the cover.

Your school library is just like Ty's library. It keeps books about the lives of real people together in one place.

7. Which of these books will most likely tell about the life of a real person?

   A. *How Bugs Live*

   B. *Little Red Riding Hood*

   C. *The Story of Jesse Owens*

8. Which of the following is a made-up book?

   A. *How Fuzzy Rabbit Got His Tail*

   B. *The True Story of Rosa Parks*

   C. *How Miley Cyrus Became a Star*

TIP 5: Some books tell true stories about the past.

Real stories about the past tell what happened long ago. They tell about people who lived long ago and what they did. Books about the past also tell why things happened.

Here are some things you could read in books about the past.

- In 1620, Pilgrims land at Plymouth Rock.
- About 1820, settlers begin moving west in covered wagons.
- In 1903, the first real airplane flies.
- About 1950, families begin watching television.
- In 1969, the first humans reach the moon.

Directions: Next to the picture of each event, write the year it happened.

9.  ____________________

10.  ____________________

11.  ____________________

Achievement Coverage: IT.C.4

12. 

____

13. 

____

TIP 6: Put the events of a story in order.

Remember the row of dominoes from Lesson 11? If you knock the first domino into the next one, the whole row will fall down, one after another.

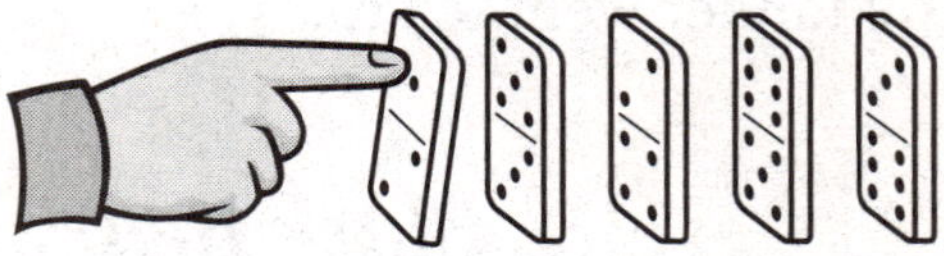

In many true stories the same kind of thing happens. Something happens first. That thing will cause something else to happen. The second thing will cause a third thing to happen, and so on.

Directions: Read the selections and answer the questions that follow.

The Oil Spill

In March, an oil tanker went to sea. It was headed west when a storm came. During the storm, the oil tanker crashed into dangerous rocks. The sea turned black as oil spilled from the tanker. Over the next weeks, many fish and birds in the area died.

14. Put these four things in the order that they happen in the selection.

_______ The oil tanker crashed into dangerous rocks.

_______ Many fish and birds were killed.

_______ Large amounts of oil spilled into the sea.

_______ An oil tanker went to sea.

Black Bears

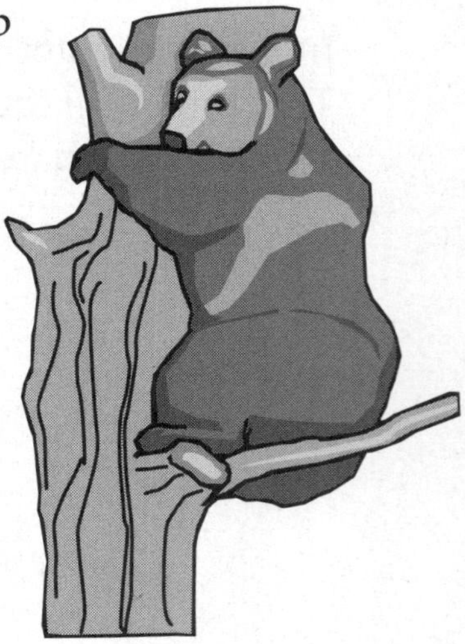

The black bear uses its strong claws to climb up a tree. It breaks off branches and throws them to the ground. When it has a small pile of branches, the bear climbs back down to eat the nuts off the branches.

15. Put these four things in the order that they happen in the selection.

_______ The bear climbs a tree.

_______ The bear eats the nuts off the branches.

_______ The bear climbs back down the tree.

_______ The bear breaks off branches and throws them to the ground.

Achievement Coverage: IT.C.4

Tell Me a True Story

Lesson 14 Summary

- True stories tell about real things and real people.
- True stories have facts that can be checked.
- Some true stories have opinions.
- Some stories tell about real people.
- Some books tell true stories about the past.
- Put the events of a true story in order.

Reading Achievement Practice begins on the following page.

Directions: Read the selection.

How Fresh Milk Gets to You

by Margaret Lujack

Where does milk come from?

If you think the story of milk begins at the grocery store, think again. You may buy it at the store, but before that, it goes through many steps on its way from the dairy farm to the dairy case.

Dairy cows eat a lot of food. Each cow eats 80 pounds of food every day. They eat grass, hay, corn and other grains. Some cows even eat breakfast cereal, potato chips and other "people food." Factories that make these foods often have extra food they cannot sell. This food is sometimes fed to cows.

A dairy cow's body takes the food and water it eats and makes milk. Cows don't start giving milk until after they have a calf (a baby cow). The calf drinks its mother's milk.

Two or three times each day, dairy cows go into a barn. A milking machine is hooked on to the cow to take out the milk. (Don't worry. It doesn't hurt!) The milk goes into a big tank. The tank cools the milk. Then it is pumped into a big, shiny tanker truck. The truck takes the milk to a dairy plant.

Go to next page

What happens at the dairy?

At the dairy plant, the milk is made ready to go to the store. First, the dairy tests the milk to make sure it is safe. Then it is heated up and quickly cooled down to kill germs. Next, much of the milk goes into jugs, bottles and cartons. Some of the milk is made into ice cream. Some of it goes into butter and yogurt. Some of it goes into cheese.

Ohio dairy cows are very busy. They produce more than four billion pounds of milk each year. So, the next time you put milk on your cereal, remember those hard-working cows and dairy farmers.

Directions: Use the selection to answer numbers 1 – 8.

1. What is this story about?

   O A. real things
   O B. made-up things
   O C. things from the past

2. When milk gets to the dairy plant, what happens to it first?

   O A. It is put into a shiny truck.
   O B. It is tested to make sure it is safe.
   O C. It is heated up and then quickly cooled down.

3. Why does the dairy heat the milk, then cool it down?

   O A. to kill germs
   O B. to make it thicker
   O C. to make it taste better

Go to next page

4. Put these four things in the order that they happen in the selection.

_____ The milk is heated, cooled and put into bottles.

_____ Machines take milk from the cows.

_____ Cows use food and water to make milk.

_____ Trucks take the milk to the dairy.

5. Complete the web with one detail from the selection.

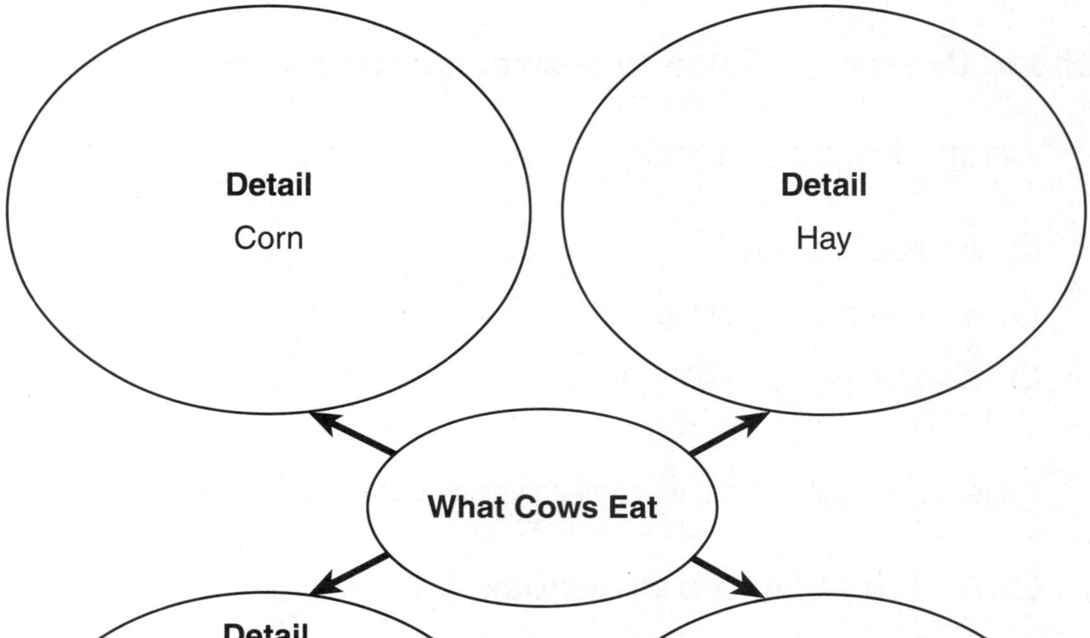

6. Factories that make these foods often have **extra** food they cannot sell.

   Circle the word that means the same as **extra**.

   - O A. more
   - O B. unsafe
   - O C. colorful

7. Which word is made from two smaller words?

   - O A. potato
   - O B. corner
   - O C. cannot

8. What does the writer think about cows?

   - O A. She thinks they are scary.
   - O B. She doesn't say what she thinks about them.
   - O C. She thinks they work very hard to give us milk.

STOP

Lesson 15: Reading Pictures

Did you know that you can read a picture? You can. In fact, pictures and drawings can be fun to read. They can show us important things. They can also show information in ways that make it easy to understand.

In this lesson, you will learn to work with graphs and drawings.

TIP 1: A picture graph uses pictures to show information.

A **graph** is a drawing that helps show information. There are lots of kinds of graphs. **Picture graphs** use pictures to show information. Each picture shows you how much of something there is.

Look at this picture graph. It shows what kinds of vegetables Farmer Bob sold at his vegetable stand.

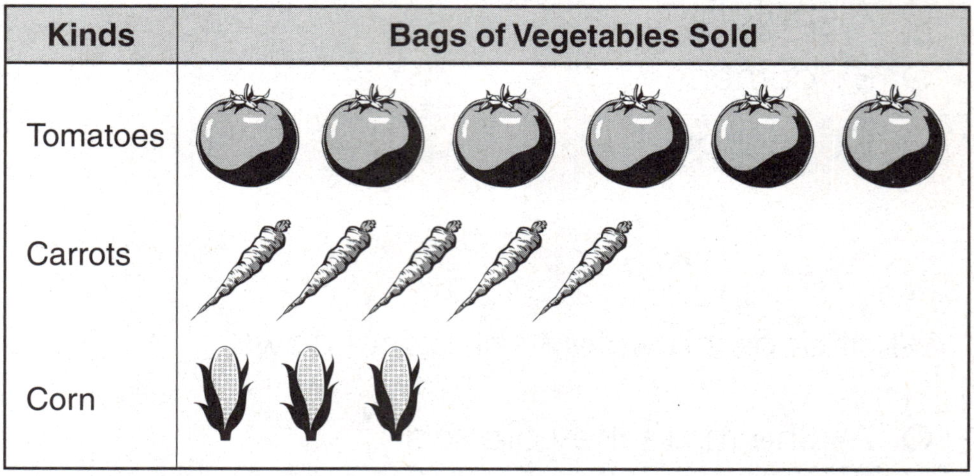

Key: Each Picture = One Bag

1. What kinds of vegetables did Farmer Bob sell?

____

____

____

The picture graph also shows how many bags of vegetables Farmer Bob sold. Each little picture stands for one bag of vegetables. Each tomato means he sold one bag of tomatoes.

2. Which vegetable did Farmer Bob sell the most bags of? (Remember that each picture stands for one bag of that kind of vegetable.)

   A. tomatoes

   B. carrots

   C. corn

3. Which vegetable did Farmer Bob sell the fewest bags of?

   A. tomatoes

   B. carrots

   C. corn

4. How many bags of carrots did Farmer Bob sell?

   A. 3

   B. 5

   C. 6

TIP 2: A circle graph looks like a pie.

Think of a pie that has been cut into pieces, or slices. You might take one slice of pie. Your dad might take two slices. It probably won't be too long before the whole pie is gone!

A **circle graph** looks like a pie. Each piece shows you how much of something there is. **Pie chart** is another name for a circle graph.

Miss Williams took her second-grade class to the library. While there, each person checked out one book.

Books Checked Out

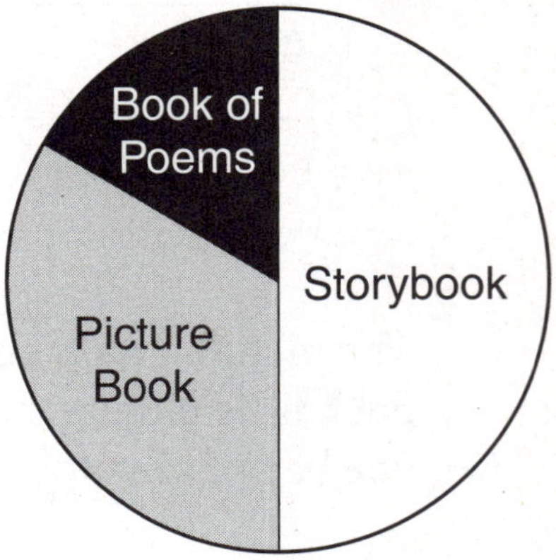

This pie chart shows that some of the class checked out storybooks, some checked out picture books, and some checked out books of poems.

The size of each piece of pie tells you more information about the people in the class. Bigger pieces of pie mean more people checked out those books. Smaller pieces of pie mean fewer people checked out those books.

5. Which kind of book did the most people check out?

   A. storybook
   B. picture book
   C. book of poems

6. Which kind of book did the fewest people check out?

   A. storybook
   B. picture book
   C. book of poems

7. Which kind of book did none of the people check out?

   A. storybook
   B. picture book
   C. joke book

Achievement Coverage: IT.D.5

TIP 3: A diagram shows the names of the different parts.

A **diagram** is a picture or drawing of something that tells the names of its parts.

When you see a baseball bat, you probably know what to call it. But you probably don't know the right names of all the bat's parts.

One way to learn the names of those parts is to look at a diagram. Here are two pictures. One is a diagram of a baseball bat. The other is a picture a batter. Look at the two pictures. Then answer Numbers 8 and 9.

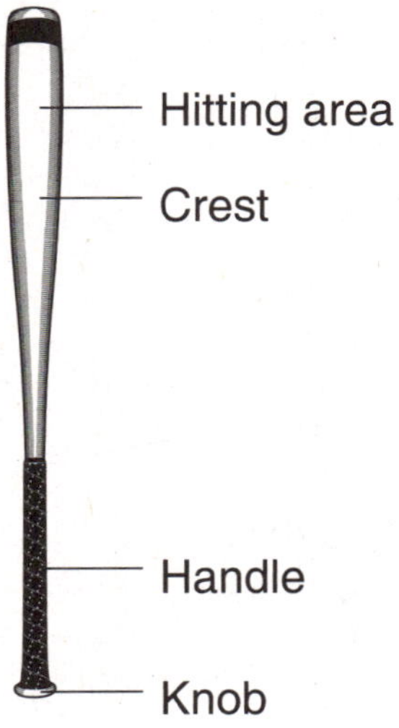

Bat

Batter

8. Which part of a bat does the batter hold?

   A. handle
   B. knob
   C. crest

9. Which part of a bat is biggest?

   A. knob
   B. handle
   C. hitting area

TIP 4: Some pictures show you how things are the same and different.

There are all kinds of pictures that give information.

Another kind of picture shows you how two things are the same and different. Look at the next picture. It shows two circles. The circles help show how birds and fish are the same and different.

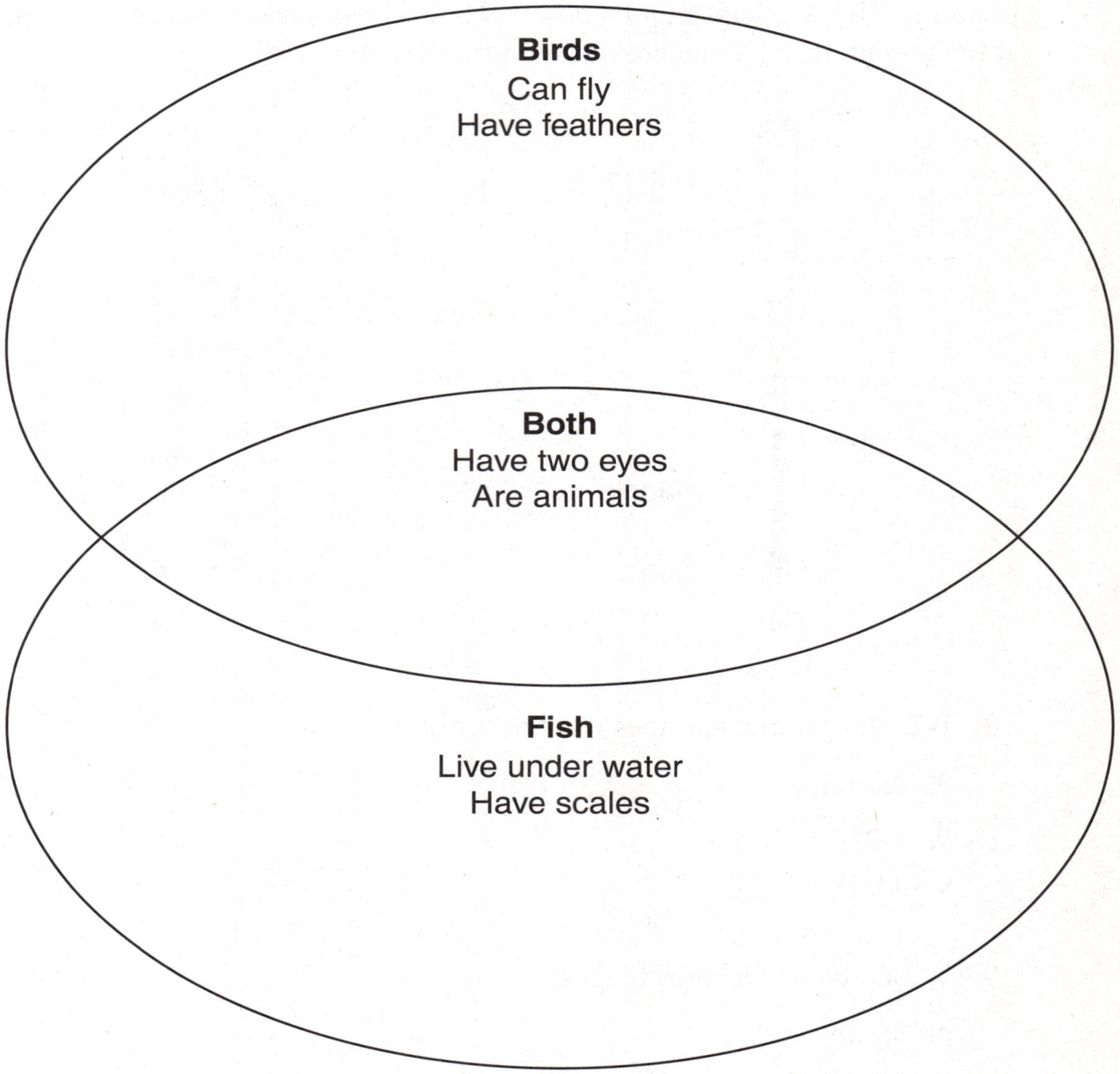

The place where the two circles touch is for information about how the two things are the same. Both birds and fish have two eyes. Both birds and fish are animals.

The places where the two circles are not together show how the two things are different. Birds have feathers. Fish do not. Birds can fly. Fish cannot.

Achievement Coverage: IT.D.5

10. Use the picture to write about another way that birds and fish are different.

Now you try.

11. Fill in the circles on the next picture. Tell how cats and dogs are the same and different.

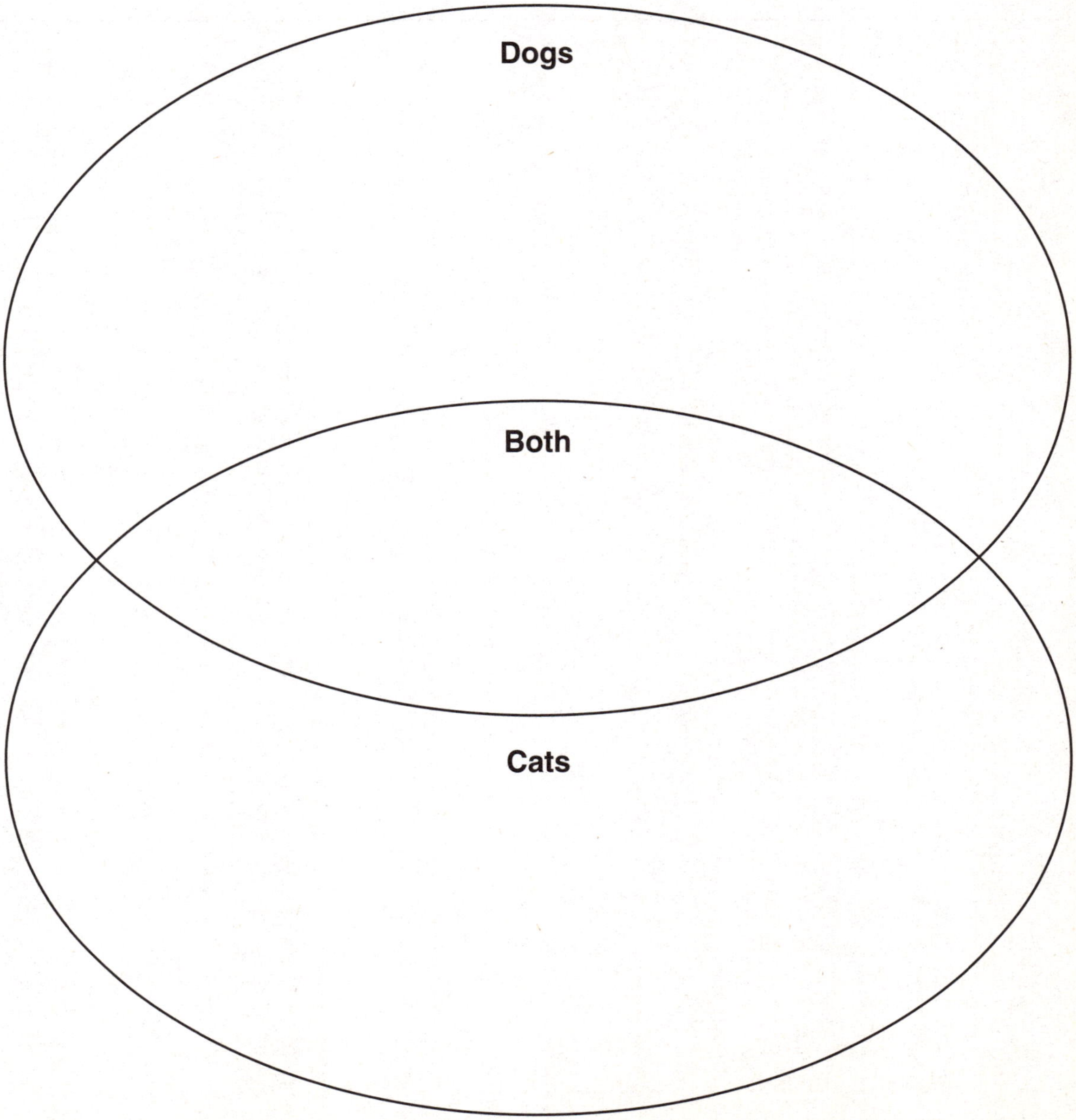

Reading Pictures

Lesson 15 Summary

When answering questions about pictures, graphs, and diagrams, remember the following tips:

- A picture graph uses pictures to show information.
- A circle graph looks like a pie.
- A diagram shows the names of the different parts.
- Some pictures show you how things are the same and different.

Reading Achievement Practice begins on the following page.

Directions: Read the selection.

Working With Animals

by Ralph Doggens

Mrs. Jewel's class is learning about different jobs. Today some people visited Mrs. Jewel's class. These people worked with animals. Each person talked about his or her job.

"I am a pet sitter," Miss Lively said. "Sometimes a family goes out of town. Their pets need to be cared for. So they call me! I feed the animals. I walk dogs and play with cats. I sing to birds. Sometimes I even stay overnight with the animals. This is a good job if you like to play with other people's pets."

"I am a dog walker," Mr. Shaw said. "Dogs need fresh air. They need exercise. Sometimes owners are too busy to take their dogs outside. That's when they call me. I take the dogs to the park. I play fetch with them. I give them treats. I walk 10 dogs a day. This is a good job if you like to be outside and love dogs. And I only work a few hours every day."

"I own a pet store," Mr. Murray said. "My pet store has food and supplies for all kinds of pets. We also have pets, of course! I know a lot about animals. My store has dogs, cats, fish, and rabbits. We also have lizards, mice, and birds. If you want to know the best food for your blue-tongued lizard, I'm the guy to ask."

"I work at a zoo," Mrs. Soren said. "I know a lot about animals too. These animals would not make good pets, though. Zoos have wild animals, like lions and bears. I work with elephants. I feed them. I wash them. I help to keep their homes clean. I also talk to people who visit the zoo. I teach them about the elephants."

Go to next page

"I am an animal doctor," Dr. Mett said. "I help animals who are sick. Some animal doctors work at zoos. If one of the elephants got sick, Mrs. Soren would tell the zoo's animal doctor. I work on a farm. I take care of horses and cows. If your pet ever gets sick, you should take it to an animal doctor. Animal doctors go to school for a long time. We know just what medicine an animal needs to feel better."

Go to next page

Directions: Use the selection, graph, and diagrams to answer questions 1 – 7.

1. Mrs. Jewel asked her class about their pets. Then she made this picture graph to show her information to the class.

Pets Belonging to Mrs. Jewel's Class

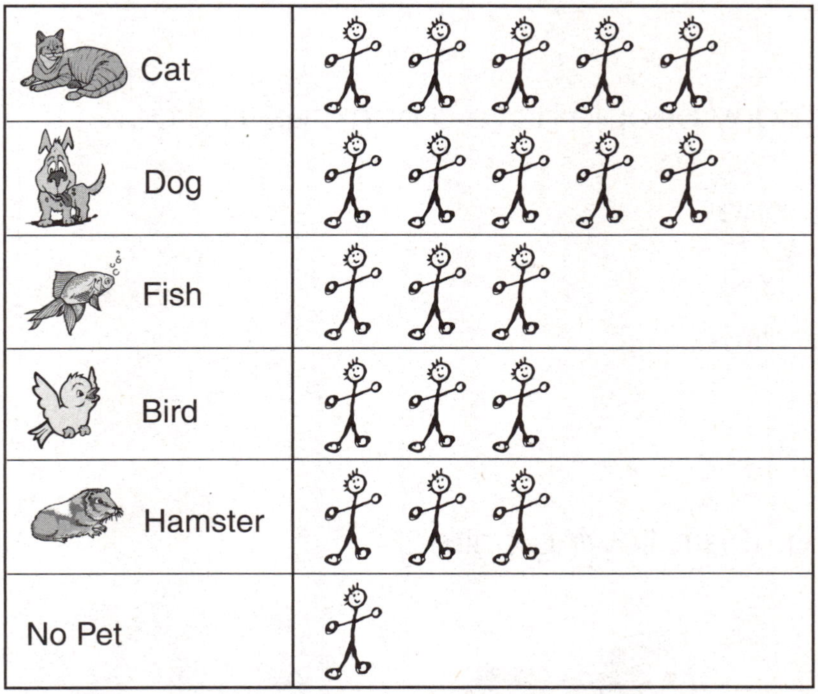

Key:  = 1 Person

Which pets do the most people have?

- O A. dogs and fish
- O B. dogs and cats
- O C. dogs and birds

Go to next page

2. How many people have no pet?

- O A. one
- O B. two
- O C. three

3. How many people have a hamster as a pet?

- O A. one
- O B. two
- O C. three

4. Look at the following animals.

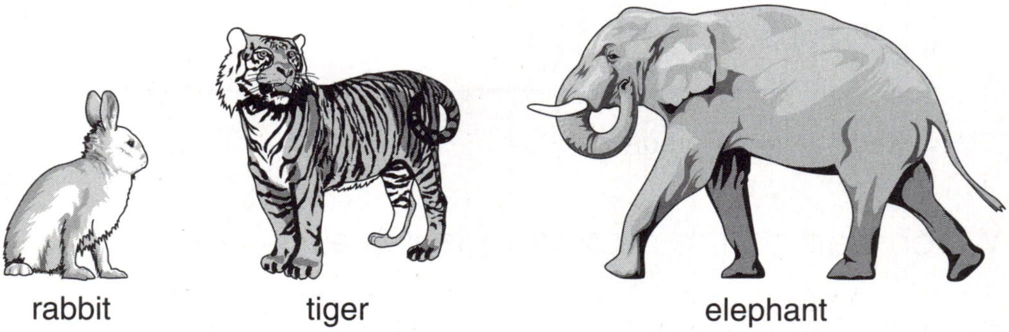

Which of these animals would you find in a pet store?

- O A. rabbit
- O B. tiger
- O C. elephant

5. Look at the circle graph that shows which jobs Mrs. Jewel's students would like to do.

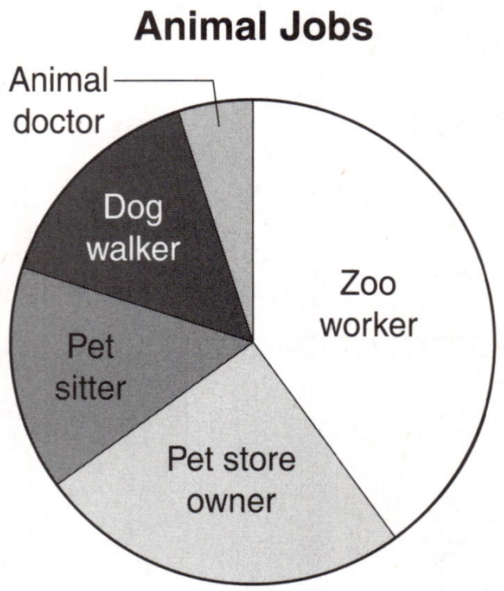

What job do the students want to do most?

- O A. zoo worker
- O B. pet sitter
- O C. animal doctor

Go to next page

6. What job do the students want to do least?

- O A. zoo worker
- O B. pet sitter
- O C. animal doctor

7. Look at this diagram of an elephant.

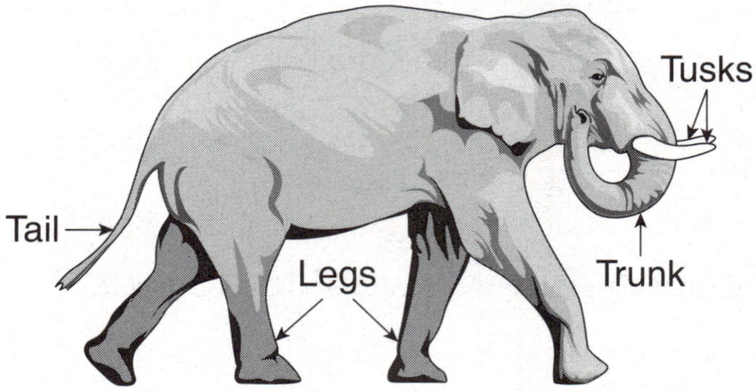

How many tusks does an elephant have?

- O A. one
- O B. two
- O C. three

8. Look at the diagram that shows how some jobs are the same and different.

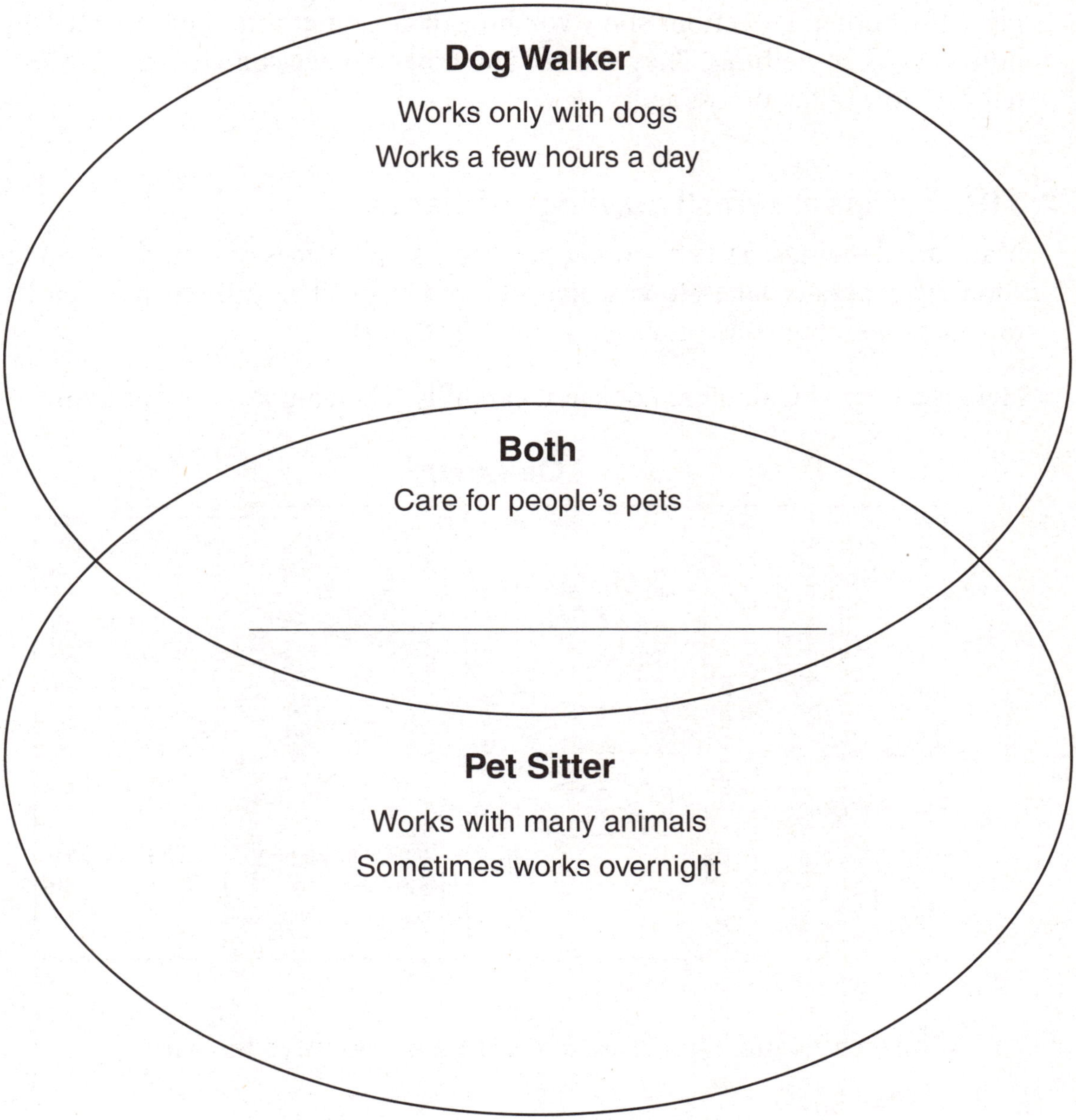

What should be written on the blank line?

- O A. play with animals
- O B. care for sick pets
- O C. wash the animals

Lesson 16: Maps and Directions

Maps and directions help you do things. Maps help you find your way from one place to another. Directions show you how to do something. They can tell you how to cook something. They can tell you how to make something. They can tell you how to do almost anything!

TIP 1: Maps are small drawings of places.

Maps are drawings. They show big places on small pieces of paper. Most maps show rivers, roads, lakes, towns, airports, and so on. There are maps of parks, towns, states, countries, and even maps of the world.

Here is a map of Oaktown. Look at it carefully. Then answer the questions.

Oaktown

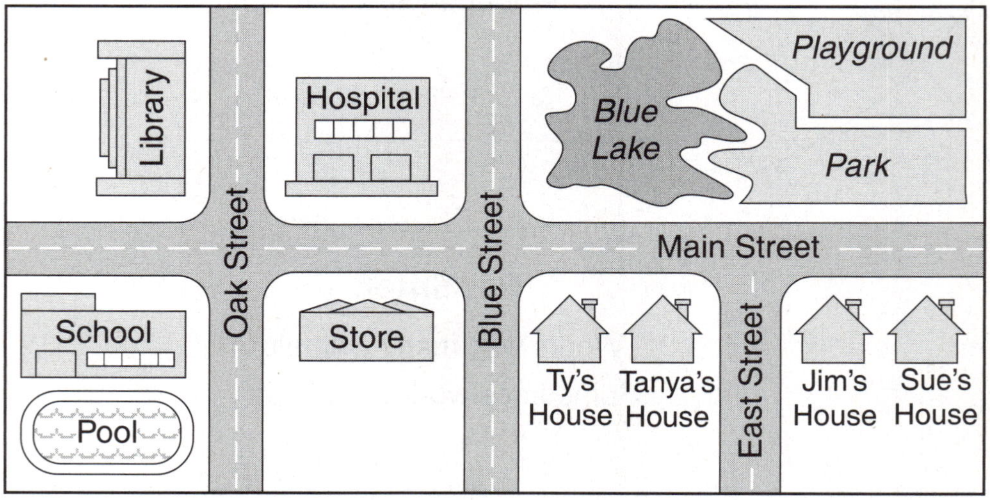

1. Which street must Jim cross to get from his house to the park?

   A. Oak Street
   B. Main Street
   C. Blue Street

2. Which street is between Tanya's house and Jim's house?

   A. East Street
   B. Main Street
   C. Blue Street

3. Which street is between the school and the store?

   A. Main Street
   B. Blue Street
   C. Oak Street

4. Which streets does Ty cross to get from his house to the swimming pool?

   A. Blue Street and Main Street
   B. East Street and Blue Street
   C. Blue Street and Oak Street

5. Which of the following is closest to the playground?

   A. the park
   B. the school
   C. the store

TIP 2: Follow directions step by step.

Directions often have steps. **Steps** tell you what to do. When following the steps to make or do something, don't forget these three rules:

- First, read each step all the way through before you begin.
- Second, go get everything you need and have it ready before you start.
- Third, follow each step in order.

Achievement Coverage: IT.C.2, IT.D.5, IT.E.6

Here are the steps you need to follow to wash your bike.

How to Wash Your Bike

Things needed: bucket, spoon, water, dish soap, rag, bike

Directions:

Step 1: Put a spoonful of dish soap in the bottom of the bucket.
Step 2: Fill the bucket with water.
Step 3: Get the rag wet.
Step 4: Clean the handle bars, seat, and frame of your bike.

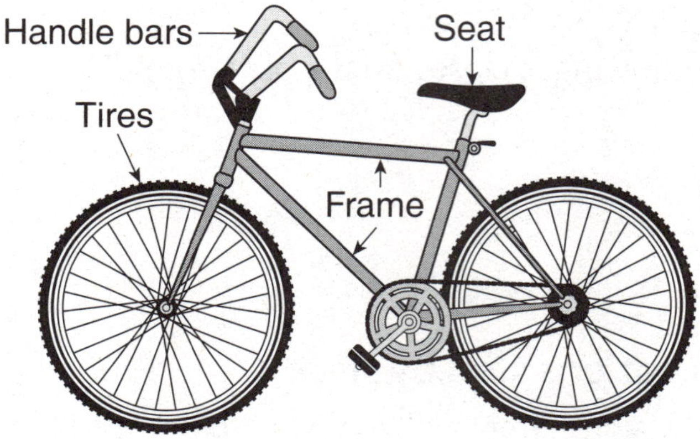

Step 5: Clean the tires.
Step 6: Dump out the soapy water and fill the bucket with clean water.
Step 7: Rinse the soap off your bike with the rag and clean water.
Step 8: Let your bike dry in the sun.

Achievement Coverage: IT.C.2, IT.D.5, IT.E.6

6. How much soap should you put in the bucket?

   A. a whole bottle

   B. a cupful

   C. a spoonful

7. What should you do after you fill the bucket with water?

   A. put soap in the bucket

   B. get the rag wet

   C. wash the handle bars

Maps and Directions

Lesson 16 Summary

When answering questions about maps and directions, remember the following tips:

- Maps are small drawings of places.
- Follow directions step by step.

Reading Achievement Practice begins on the following page.

R Reading Achievement Practice

Directions: Look at the map.

Sparkle Lake

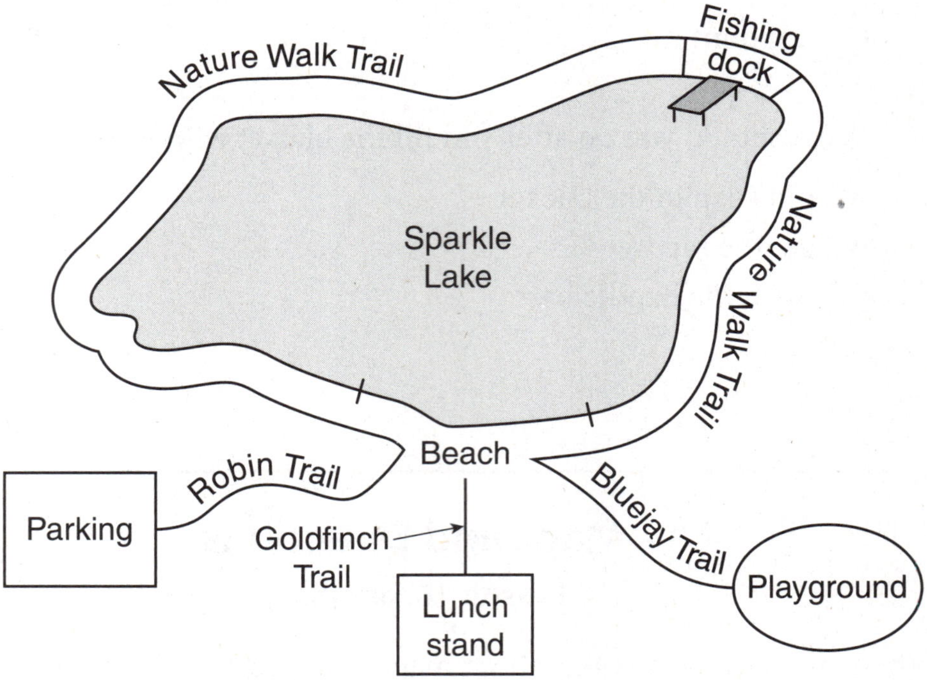

Directions: Use the following map to answer questons 1 – 3.

1. What trail should you take to get from the beach to the lunch stand?

   O A. Robin Trail

   O B. Goldfinch Trail

   O C. Bluejay Trail

2. What trail should you take to get from the fishing dock to the beach?

   - O A. Nature Walk Trail
   - O B. Robin Trail
   - O C. Goldfinch Trail

3. What trail goes around the whole lake?

   - O A. Robin Trail
   - O B. Bluejay Trail
   - O C. Nature Walk Trail

Directions: Read the selection.

How to Make a Peanut Butter and Jelly Sandwich

Things needed:

- 2 slices of bread
- peanut butter
- jelly
- a knife

What to do:

Step 1: Use the knife to put peanut butter on one side of a bread slice.

Step 2: Use the knife to put jelly on one side of the other bread slice.

Step 3: Put the two slices together so the peanut butter and jelly are stuck to each other.

Step 4: Eat your sandwich.

Directions: Use the selection to answer questions 4 – 5.

4. What do the directions say you should use the knife for?

   O A. to cut the sandwich
   O B. to put peanut butter and jelly on the bread
   O C. to open the jar of jelly

5. What should you do after you put the two slices together?

   O A. Put peanut butter on one side of a bread slice.
   O B. Put jelly on one side of another bread slice.
   O C. Eat your sandwich.

Unit 5

Reading for Fun

What kind of stories do you like best? Scary stories? Animal stories? Stories about friends? Do you like to make up your own stories or read stories written by someone else?

This unit will help you see what makes a good story. You will learn about characters, setting, and plot. You'll also learn about poems. Poems can also tell stories. Once you've learned all about stories, you might want to write one of your own. Go ahead . . . tell me a story!

In This Unit

Achievement Coverage: LT.A.1, LT.A.3, LT.B.2, LT.C.4

Lesson 17: Tell Me a Made-Up Story

Read the following made-up story. Pay close attention. You will use it in this lesson.

Mrs. Jefferson's Scary Story

Mrs. Patty Jefferson sat behind her desk and waited for the room to get quiet. Finally, she said, "Each of you has written a story. Today, you will read your story to the class. Before you begin, I will read you a story I wrote when I was a little girl."

She took an old notebook from her desk. She asked one of the students to close the window shade. She did not want the sun to come in. The class held their breath. When the room was dark, she began.

"A very scary thing happened to some people," she said. "They were frightened. The End."

The students looked at each other.

"All right, class. Now each of you may read the story you wrote."

"Mrs. Jefferson! That wasn't a real story," Kenny said. "We don't know anything about the people. Tell us about the **characters**. Who were they? Tell us how they looked and what they did."

"Your story doesn't tell us what happened," Ben said, sounding very unhappy. "A story has to have a **plot**. Tell us about what happened and why it happened."

"Yeah," said Mari. "We don't even know when the story happened or where it happened. We want to know about the **setting**. Tell us when and where everything happened."

TIP 1: Made-up stories always have characters.

Made-up stories always have characters. The **characters** are the people in the story. Sometimes characters are animals. Anyone who is in a story is a character.

On the lines below, write down the names of all the characters from "Mrs. Jefferson's Scary Story."

____

____

____

1. Which of the following characters from the story is a teacher?

   A. Ben
   B. Patty
   C. Mari

TIP 2: Made-up stories always have a setting.

The **setting** is the time and place a story happens. Look around you. Where are you right now? At school? At home? In a desk? On a floor? Is it daytime? Is it night? Where is your setting?

2. What is the setting of "Mrs. Jefferson's Scary Story"?

   A. a classroom during the day
   B. a playground at night
   C. Mrs. Jefferson's house during the day

TIP 3: Something always happens in a story.

Why did Mrs. Jefferson's students not like her story? Because nothing happened! If nothing happens in a story, then the story won't go very far.

Plot is what happens in a story. A plot is sometimes called the action. Plot may be the first thing you think of before starting to write a story.

Read the sentences. Each sentence is from a different story. Write whether the sentence tells mostly about characters, setting, or plot.

Write *C* for characters, *S* for setting, or *P* for plot.

_____ 3. Jeff and his dog are both eight years old.

_____ 4. The family was sleeping when the fire alarm went off.

_____ 5. The forest was dark and quiet.

_____ 6. It was 5 o'clock on Monday morning.

_____ 7. The rabbit stopped and fell into the hole.

TIP 4: Details tell you more about the characters.

You learned about details in lesson 6. Details can tell you what characters look like. Details can also tell you what characters think and feel.

Read the story below. Pay close attention to the details. Then answer Numbers 8 and 9.

Uncle Charlie is tall and thin. When he sits down, his arms and legs fold up like a folding chair. Uncle Charlie has a shiny pink head and a little ring of hair just above his ears. He says he grew so fast that he pushed his head up through his hair. Uncle Charlie likes to laugh. He's always happy, and he makes me happy when I'm with him.

Uncle Willie is short and round. When he sits in our big stuffed chair, his feet barely touch the floor. Uncle Willie has snow-white hair. He is very quiet and doesn't laugh much. When he does laugh, his face gets as red as a fire truck. Most of the time I can't tell if Uncle Willie is happy or sad.

8. Circle the drawing that looks most like Uncle Charlie.

A. B. C.

9. Which word best tells about Uncle Willie?

   A. quiet
   B. angry
   C. cheerful

TIP 5: Stories can have more than one setting.

Every story has a setting. Long stories and books may have many different settings. If you read the details carefully, they will tell you when and where each part of the story takes place.

Read the following two stories about a park and a beach. Then answer Numbers 10 through 13.

Sunnyside State Park

The gate to Sunnyside State Park was closed and locked. Morning sunlight peeked through the tall trees. Flowers were starting to open up to the sun. A warm wind blew through the playground. It was early, and the park was empty.

Sandy Beach

Sandy Beach was crawling with people. Some splashed in the water. Some played games. Others lay on bright beach towels and slept in the afternoon sunlight. A man in a large white hat sold balloons to the children. Every now and then a child's balloon would get away, floating up into the clear summer sky.

10. What is the setting for the first story?

    A. a park
    B. a farm
    C. a lake

11. When does the first story take place?

    A. winter
    B. spring
    C. fall

12. Which is one way "Sunnyside State Park" is different from "Sandy Beach"?

    A. The park is empty, but the beach is crowded.
    B. The park is open, but the beach is closed.
    C. There are balloons in the park, but there are towels at the beach.

13. During what time of year does the second story take place?

    A. fall
    B. spring
    C. summer

TIP 6: The plot also tells why the action happens.

Most stories have a beginning, middle, and end.

- The **beginning** tells about the characters, the setting, and the problems the characters must fix.
- The **middle** tells how the characters try to solve the problems.
- The **end** tells how the problems are solved.

The main character might have a problem with another character. It might be a parent, a neighbor, or maybe a big bad wolf.

The problem could also be with a thing. It might be a snowstorm, a broken swing, or a rocky hill.

Sometimes, a character has a problem within himself or herself. A child might want to be brave in the dark. Or, a bike rider might need to pick a path to take.

Read this story about a boy who loved trains. Look for Michael's problem. Then answer the questions that follow.

The Boy Who Loved Trains

by Nikki Lake

Michael loved trains. He had wooden trains, plastic trains, paper trains, and wind-up trains. But Michael wanted another kind of train.

Michael wanted a train that could run on its own. He wanted the one he had seen at Toy City. It had seven cars and a flashing light. The train could make real puffs of smoke as it went along the track.

"You already have too many trains," Michael's father said. But Michael didn't think he had too many trains.

"One train is as good as another," his mother said.

But one train wasn't as good as another to Michael. No one understood how much Michael wanted that train.

Then one day Michael's grandfather came to visit. He gave Michael a large box.

Sometimes, it's fun to think ahead while you're reading. Let's try that now.

14. What do you think is in the box that Grandfather gives Michael?

____

____

____

____

Now, read the rest of the story to see if you were right.

Michael set his trains on the floor and took the box. He could feel something moving inside. Then he saw a wet nose pushing through one of the air holes in the lid. He opened the box. Inside was a brown puppy. Michael gave his grandfather a big hug and thanked him. Then he ran outside with his furry new friend. He left his trains on the floor behind him.

15. Did you guess correctly or did the writer fool you?

____

____

____

____

16. What is Michael's main problem in the story?

    A. He does not like trains anymore.
    B. He wants a train that can run on its own.
    C. He thinks he has too many trains.

17. What problem does Michael's father have in the story?

    A. He thinks Michael has too many trains.
    B. He doesn't like trains that puff smoke.
    C. He thinks trains cost too much money.

18. When does Michael's grandfather give him the puppy?

    A. before the story begins
    B. at the beginning of the story
    C. at the end of the story

What if the writer had written a different ending? What would you think about Michael if the author had written this as the story's last paragraph?

> Michael set his trains on the floor and took the box. He pulled the lid off and looked inside. He said, "Hey, a new truck! Thanks, Grandpa. It's pretty neat." Michael took the truck out and pushed it around a little. Then he went back to playing with his trains.

19. What does this new ending tell us?

    A. Michael hoped that his grandfather would get him a truck.

    B. Michael likes his trains more than he likes the truck.

    C. Michael no longer likes playing with trains.

Tell Me a Made-Up Story

Lesson 17 Summary

- Made-up stories always have characters.
- Made-up stories always have a setting.
- Something always happens in a story.
- Details tell you more about the characters.
- Stories can have more than one setting.
- The plot also tells why the action happens.

Reading Achievement Practice begins on the following page.

Directions: Read the selection.

Marvin's Ride

by Natalie Miller

Marvin peeked from his mouse hole in the wall at 444 Daisy Drive. The little girl was skateboarding in the front hall again. Oh, boy! Marvin wanted to skateboard more than anything.

One day while the little girl was at school, Marvin called his friends. They pushed the girl's bright red skateboard into the driveway. Marvin jumped on and yelled, "Give me a BIG PUSH, please!" So, Marvin's little mouse friends did just that. Marvin shot down the driveway and flew into the street.

The skateboard tore down Daisy Drive. "Oh, nooo!" Marvin screamed.

"Where are the brakes?" Marvin cried. He skated past a stop sign and ran right into a mail carrier. Letters flew into the air like snowflakes.

Marvin shut his eyes tightly. He was going faster and faster. The skateboard zoomed through the open doorway of Sid's Bowl-A-Rama.

Go to next page

Marvin opened his eyes. He was sailing down a bowling alley. He was headed straight for 10 huge pins. He was lined up perfectly. CRASH! BOOM! BANG! Pins flew wildly in every direction.

Marvin hung on for dear life as an angry man threw the skateboard out the back door. He climbed on top of the board just as it hit a bump and crashed.

"The skateboard is a mess," Marvin cried. "How will I get home? Oh, dear!"

Marvin slowly walked back to 444 Daisy Drive. He called his little mouse friends together. They helped him push and pull and tug the little girl's skateboard home.

Afterward, Marvin crawled into his hole in the wall. He needed rest. He needed to think. Marvin lay on his tiny mouse bed for three hours. Then he made a choice. From now on, he would stay away from all things with wheels.

And that is just what Marvin did.

Directions: Use the selection to answer questions 1 – 8.

1. Where does this story begin?

   O A. on Fourth Street

   O B. at 444 Daisy Drive

   O C. in Sid's Bowl-A-Rama

2. Which of these events happens first?

   ○ A. Marvin gets thrown out the back door.
   ○ B. Marvin rolls through Sid's Bowl-A-Rama.
   ○ C. Marvin runs into a mail carrier.

3. What causes Marvin to cry out, "Where are the brakes?"

   ○ A. He can't stop the skateboard.
   ○ B. He wants to stop at Sid's Bowl-A-Rama.
   ○ C. He needs to get back to Daisy Drive.

4. Which of the following best tells about Marvin's ride?

   ○ A. He has a wild ride on a skateboard.
   ○ B. He runs into a mail carrier.
   ○ C. He crashes into 10 bowling pins.

5. What is Marvin's main problem in the story?

   ○ A. A man gets angry with him.
   ○ B. His friends won't help him.
   ○ C. He can't stop the skateboard.

Go to next page

6. Which of these is a setting from "Marvin's Ride"?

- O A. a hole in the wall
- O B. a kitchen counter
- O C. a shelf at a toy store

7. Why will Marvin probably stay away from roller skates?

- O A. because he's afraid of falling
- O B. because they are too large for a mouse
- O C. because they have wheels

8. Which word best tells about Marvin?

- O A. mean
- O B. scared
- O C. big

STOP

Achievement Coverage: LT.C.4

Lesson 18: Words That Sing

Songs are poems set to music.

But did you know that many poems can "sing" without music?

This lesson will show you how poems use words to "sing" us a song. It will also show you how poems can paint pictures in our minds. This lesson will show you how poems can be different from other types of writing. Most of all, it will show you how poems can be fun to read.

Read "The Blanket Tent." It will help you understand this lesson.

The Blanket Tent

by Mike Acton

How we love the smell of a summer's day
In the shade of our blanket tent
Where we've flattened the yellow dandelions
And rolled till the grass is bent.

We pretend to go on safari trips
And to camp along jungle streams
Where we listen to bright-colored birds that call
To us through a vine-covered dream.

Or sometimes we camp in the Arctic ice,
Where it's fifty degrees below,
And we shiver and shake in our blanket tent
While our sled dogs sleep in the snow.

But sometimes we play at nothing at all.
We just lie on our backs and stare
At the ragged old blanket above us,
Which shelters the worlds we share.

TIP 1: Read the poem again and again.

Poets write about things they have seen and heard. They want you to see and hear those same things when you read their poems.

Read "The Blanket Tent" one more time. Let the words make pictures in your mind as you read.

Do you see how the poem is written in groups of four lines? A **stanza** is a group of lines.

After you have finished reading the poem, draw a picture about something from the second or third stanza. Draw your picture in the box below.

1.

Achievement Coverage: LT.C.4

TIP 2: Listen for the music of the poem.

Some poems make music with words. You hear a musical beat because of how the poets say things.

You have heard the music of poetry ever since you were a baby. Before you could read you may have heard such rhymes as this:

Five Little Monkeys

a Nursery Rhyme

Five little monkeys jumping on the bed.
One fell off and bumped his head.
Momma called the doctor and the doctor said,
"No more monkeys jumping on the bed!"

Four little monkeys jumping on the bed.
One fell off and bumped his head.
Momma called the doctor and the doctor said,
"No more monkeys jumping on the bed!"

Three little monkeys jumping on the bed.
One fell off and bumped his head.
Momma called the doctor and the doctor said,
"No more monkeys jumping on the bed!"

Two little monkeys jumping on the bed.
One fell off and bumped his head.
Momma called the doctor and the doctor said,
"No more monkeys jumping on the bed!"

One little monkey jumping on the bed.
One fell off and bumped his head.
Momma called the doctor and the doctor said,
"No more monkeys jumping on the bed!"

Can you hear the musical beat in the poem above? This is called **rhythm**.

Follow along as your teacher reads "Choosing Shoes." Listen to the music that the words make with their rhythm.

Choosing Shoes

New shoes, new shoes,
Red and pink and blue shoes.
Tell me, what would you choose,
If they'd let us buy?

Buckle shoes, bow shoes,
Pretty pointy-toe shoes,
Strappy, cappy low shoes;
Let's have some to try.

Bright shoes, white shoes,
Dandy-dance-by-night shoes,
Perhaps a little tight shoes,
Like some? So would I.

But

Flat shoes, fat shoes,
Stump-along-like-that shoes,
Wipe-them-on-the-mat shoes,
That's the sort they'll buy.

Achievement Coverage: LT.C.4

TIP 3: Watch and listen for words that rhyme.

Rhyming words are words that have the same sound. Many poems have words that sound the same at the ends of lines. Here are some examples of rhyming words:

hat / cat

bed / head

you / through

box / fox

go / snow

In "Choosing Shoes" on page 194, the words *shoes* and *choose* are rhyming words.

2. What other rhyming words can you find in "Choosing Shoes"?

____

3. Write a rhyming word for each of the following:

blue ____

day ____

tree ____

fly ____

A **poet** is someone who writes poems. Help the poet of the next poem by circling the correct rhyming words to finish this poem.

If You Are Looking for a Mouse

If you are looking for a mouse,
Don't try to find one in my __________.

(tree / house / shoe)

The mouse that lived here ran away
When Tom the cat came here to __________.

(stay / sleep / live)

TIP 4: Remember to use your five senses.

Writers use special words to help the reader feel, taste, hear, see, and smell what they are writing about.

Here are some examples of these special words at work in short sentences.

Feel My pillow is <u>as soft as a cloud</u>.

Taste The lemon is <u>so sour it makes my tongue curl</u>.

Hear The birds sound <u>like they have bells in their throats</u>.

See The raindrops look <u>like tiny diamonds</u>.

Smell The dog smells <u>like an old sock</u>.

Look at the following example. Then complete the sentences with your own special words.

The apple tastes <u>juicy and sweet</u>.

4. The clouds look ______________________________.

5. The rose smells ______________________________.

6. The thunder sounds ______________________________.

Achievement Coverage: LT.D.5

TIP 5: Look for the main idea in the poem.

Poems are like other kinds of writing. They tell things that happen. They tell about feelings. They can be scary or happy or sad. Every poem has some kind of main idea.

When you first read a poem, you may not understand every word. Just try to find out what the poem is mainly about. Then read the poem again to be sure about what each line means.

Read the next poem carefully. Think about what the poem is mainly about.

Old Mother Duck

by Robyn Winchell

Old mother duck walked down the road,
Three ducklings in the back.
They waddled close behind her
Saying quack, quack, quack.

They followed her across the lawn
And down the garden path,
And when she slid into the pond
They followed—splash, splash, splash.

7. What is this poem mostly about?

   A. three little ducks crossing the lawn

   B. three little ducks splashing in the pond

   C. three little ducks following their mother

Words that Sing

Lesson 18 Summary

When answering questions about poetry, remember the following tips:

- Read the poem again and again.
- Listen for the music of the poem.
- Watch and listen for words that rhyme.
- Remember to use your five senses.
- Look for the main idea in the poem.

Reading Achievement Practice begins on the following page.

Directions: Read the poem.

Ladybugs and Tumblebugs

by Mickey Toom

hollyhocks

I spent most all of yesterday
Behind the poplar trees
And crawling through the hollyhocks
On busy hands and knees.

I saw a hundred moving things!
You wouldn't think there'd be
So many funny-looking bugs
That creeped around like me.

I couldn't tell by watching them
Exactly what they did,
Or where they went as they passed by,
Or why they sometimes hid.

Go to next page

I saw ladybugs and tumblebugs—
Green bugs, red, and brown—
Giant bugs and tiny bugs,
And bugs that flew around.

I splashed back again this morning
To the poplar trees to see
If the busy bugs of yesterday
Would still remember me.

But when I reached my watching place,
There were no bugs to see.
Just raindrops sparkling on the grass
And hollyhocks—and me.

Directions: Use the poem to answer questions 1 – 5.

1. What is the main idea of the poem?

   ○ A. Flowers get wet in the rain.
   ○ B. Some bugs hide from people.
   ○ C. A boy watches busy bugs.

2. Why are there no bugs to watch on the second day?

   ○ A. The rain made the bugs hide.
   ○ B. The bugs are still asleep.
   ○ C. It is too hot outside for the bugs.

3. In the first stanza of "Ladybugs and Tumblebugs," which words rhyme?

 - O A. yesterday / trees
 - O B. trees / knees
 - O C. yesterday / hollyhocks

4. Which of the following is true about the poem "Ladybugs and Tumblebugs"?

 - O A. The poem has three stanzas.
 - O B. The poem has a musical beat.
 - O C. The poem does not have rhyming words.

5. Read these lines from the poem.

> But when I reached my watching place,
> There were no bugs to see.
> Just raindrops **sparkling** on the grass
> And hollyhocks—and me.

Which word means about the same as the word **sparkling**?

 - O A. shining
 - O B. shaking
 - O C. climbing

STOP

Lesson 19: Writing Your Answers

In this book, you have answered a lot of questions that ask you to pick an answer. You have also written your own answers to some questions.

When you write your own answer, be sure to read a story's details closely. Then read each question carefully, and write a complete answer.

Read this story. It will help you answer questions that ask you to write in sentences.

A Great Day at the Beach

by Stacey Craig

When Traci first woke up it was raining and thundering. "Oh no," she thought. "This is the day Mother and I were going to the beach!" Traci was unhappy, but it wasn't long before she was fast asleep again. When she woke up a second time, her mother was calling, "Traci. Get up. Hurry. Let's go to the beach." The rain had stopped and it was sunny.

Traci and her dog, Sam, ran along the edge of the water. The wet sand felt almost cool. Sometimes she stopped to watch her footprints fill with seawater. Once, she lay on her back and made a "sand angel." It filled up with water, too.

A little while later, Traci decided to make a "snowman" out of sand. She stuck on two sand dollars for his eyes. Then she found a long, pointy, pink seashell for the sandman's nose. For his mouth, she used smooth, colored pebbles that had washed up on the shore. She made the sandman's arms from pieces of driftwood. Finally, Traci put her floppy hat and sunglasses on the sandman. He looked great! Even Sam seemed to like Mr. Sandman.

Later, a big wave of water surprised Sam. He shook his whole body to dry off. Traci laughed. The spray felt good on her hot skin. But a man sitting in a beach chair did not like getting wet. And he certainly did NOT like having his newspaper splashed!

By this time, Traci was getting tired. "The best place to be now," she thought, "is under Mom's beach umbrella." "Come on, Sam!" she called. She and Sam started back up the beach toward a tiny dot of yellow. It was her mother's umbrella.

When they finally reached the yellow beach umbrella, her mother asked, "Did you have fun?"

"Yes," Traci said with a grin. "This has been my best beach day ever."

TIP 1: Understand the question.

Some test questions ask you to write in complete sentences. You can spot this kind of question because you will be given at least two writing lines for your answer.

The first step in writing a good answer is to read the question again and again until you are sure you know what it is asking. As you read, watch for any key words in the question. Some key words are *when*, *where*, *why*, *how many*, *compare* and *describe*.

Read the following question. Circle any key words.

Why was Traci unhappy at the beginning of the story?

When you are sure you understand the question, answer it below. Remember, you can reread the question as many times as you need.

The answer has been started for you. Since this is a "why" question, you will write a "because" answer.

1. Why was Traci unhappy at the beginning of the story?

   Traci was unhappy at the beginning of the story because

   ____

   ____

TIP 2: Write a complete answer.

When you are asked to write an answer, make sure to answer all parts of the question fully.

When you write your own answers, use details from the story.

Read the question and Heather and Juan's answers below.

What did Sam do after he was hit by a wave of water?

Heather's answer—

shook

Juan's answer—

Sam shook his whole body, spraying water all over Traci. He also splashed water all over a man and his newspaper.

2. Check the name of the student whose answer is more complete.

☐ Heather ☐ Juan

TIP 3: Explain your answer.

Sometimes you will be asked to write a two-part answer. The first part will ask you to write an answer. The second part will ask you to explain your answer.

Here is an example of that kind of question. Answer it using details from the story. Remember to write in complete sentences.

3. Think about the story "A Great Day at the Beach." What is Traci like while she is at the beach?

____

____

What is one idea from the story that shows what Traci is like while she is at the beach?

____

____

Achievement Coverage: RP.E.6

Writing Your Answers

Lesson 19 Summary

When writing your answers, remember the following tips:

- Understand the question.
- Write a complete answer.
- Explain your answer.

Reading Achievement Practice begins on the following page.

Directions: Read the selection.

Bones Like Stones

by Rick Zollo

Neil was with his father one Saturday afternoon. They took a drive out into the country. They stopped at a park with a lake. At the end of the lake was a big dam.

"See the dam," said Dad.

"It holds back the lake," said Neil.

"Right. The water behind the dam isn't only a lake."

"What else is it?" asked Neil.

"It's also called a reservoir. A reservoir holds water for people to drink."

"We drink that water?"

"It depends," said Dad. "Drinking water comes from a lot of places."

Neil thought about it for a second. It was a lot for him to understand. He looked at the dam again. "What's it made of?" he asked.

"Cement. Cement is made from powder and crushed rock and sand. It's mixed with water and poured into metal forms. When it dries, it gets hard like stone."

"Oh, boy," said Neil. "I fell on the sidewalk the other day. It was made of cement. I scraped my knee and it really hurt."

Go to next page

Neil and Dad walked away from the dam to a dry riverbed. People were walking around, looking at big and small stones. Dad led Neil to a big long stone. He bent over it and pointed to something. "See this?" asked Dad.

Neil saw what looked like a spider web scratched into the stone. "What is it?" asked Neil.

"It was once a shell of a sea creature. Many years ago, this place was at the bottom of the sea. This shell is called a fossil."

"Fossil? It's part of the stone."

"That's right."

"Dad, remember when we went to the museum?"

"Yes."

"And we saw all those dinosaur bones? Those bones are fossils, too!"

"Good point, son! They were found in places like this, places that were once underground or under water. The dinosaur bones were part of the rocks and sand."

"They were bones like stones," said Neil.

"Yes, bones like stones." Dad replied.

Neil looked at the people staring at fossils in stones. He looked over at the cement dam. He smiled and thought, "There's so much to know."

Go to next page

Directions: Use the selection to answer questions 1 – 10

1. When did Neil go to the park with his father?

____

____

2. Why is the water behind the dam called a reservoir?

____

____

3. How does Neil probably feel when he remembers the visit to the museum?

____

____

What is one idea from the story that shows how Neil probably feels after he remembers the visit to the museum?

____

____

Go to next page

4. What kind of a person is Neil's Dad?

____

____

What is one idea from the story that shows what kind of a person he is?

____

____

5. Which word has the same vowel sound as the word **lake**?

- O A. water
- O B. that
- O C. place

6. This is a sentence from the story.

"**It's** mixed with water and poured into metal forms."

It's is a contraction for which words?

- O A. It is
- O B. It has
- O C. It does

Go to next page

7. This is a sentence from the story.

"I **scraped** my knee and it really hurt."

What does **scraped** mean?

- O A. fit
- O B. hid
- O C. cut

8. This is a sentence from the story.

"'Yes, bones like stones.' Dad **replied**."

Which word means the opposite of **replied**?

- O A. heard
- O B. spoke
- O C. tried

9. What is this selection about?

____

____

List three details that support the main idea.

A. ____________________________________

____

B. ____________________________________

____

C. ____________________________________

____

10. Where is a place that fossils are found?

- O A. in powder
- O B. in spider webs
- O C. in dry riverbeds

Appendix

Word Power Log

Using the Word Power Log will help you become a better reader. As you come across new words, write them on the lines below. When you have time, look them up in a dictionary. Then write their meanings on the lines provided.

Word: ____________________

Meaning: ____________________

____

Word: ____________________

Meaning: ____________________

____

Word: ____________________

Meaning: ____________________

____

Word: ____________________

Meaning: ____________________

____

Word: ____________________

Meaning: ____________________

____

Word: ____________________

Meaning: ____________________

____

Word: ______________________________

Meaning: ______________________________

____

Word: ______________________________

Meaning: ______________________________

____

Word: ______________________________

Meaning: ______________________________

____

Word: ______________________________

Meaning: ______________________________

____

Word: ______________________________

Meaning: ______________________________

____

Word: ______________________________

Meaning: ______________________________

____

Word: ______________________________

Meaning: ______________________________

____

Word: ____

Meaning: ______________________________________

____

Word: ____

Meaning: ______________________________________

____

Word: ____

Meaning: ______________________________________

____

Word: ____

Meaning: ______________________________________

____

Word: ____

Meaning: ______________________________________

____

Word: ____

Meaning: ______________________________________

____

Word: ____

Meaning: ______________________________________

____

Activity Pages

Use with page 102.

Use with page 128.